ANALYTICAL BIOLOGY

BY

G. SOMMERHOFF

OXFORD UNIVERSITY PRESS
LONDON: GEOFFREY CUMBERLEGE
1950

Oxford University Press, Amen House, London E.C. 4

GLASGOW NEW YORK TORONTO MELBOURNE WELLINGTON
BOMBAY CALCUTTA MADRAS CAPE TOWN

Geoffrey Cumberlege, Publisher to the University

PRINTED IN GREAT BRITAIN

PREFACE

ALTHOUGH the controversy between vitalism and mechanism
is dead, the distinctive directiveness and orderliness of organic
activities has remained a source of perplexing problems in
philosophy and science. We have come a long way since
Aristotle first claimed the distinguishing character of the living
organism as a whole to be the 'absence of haphazard and con-
ductiveness of everything to an end'. But in some respects we
still have a long way to go. Aristotle attributed this directiveness and orderliness of living beings to the activity of their
souls, and the ladder of beings which he recognized in the
scale of nature was essentially a hierarchy of such souls.
To-day we explain these properties of the living organism in
terms of its 'organization', and we describe the fundamental
thread that runs through the history of our living world as a
continuous rise in the 'levels of organization'. But can we
honestly claim to have an adequate conception of what we
mean by 'organization' in this biological sense?

When the physicist refers to the 'organization' of the atoms
in a molecule or crystal, he has in mind a fairly definite concept
and refers to a type of spatial order for which there exists a
mathematical measure. But in biology the concept of organization refers to something different and far less definite. When
we say that an ant colony has a higher degree of organization
than a swarm of locusts, or when we speak of a malignant
tumour as an unorganized proliferation of cells, we are not
primarily thinking of this type of spatial order at all. Rather,
we are thinking of the coordination, integration, and purposiveness which distinguish the behaviour of the ants from
that of the locusts, or the differentiation of healthy cells from
that of malignant tissue. What then is this directiveness and
biological orderliness? Can it be reduced to physical terms, or,
as some biologists believe, is it an irreducible characteristic of
living systems? Can we find a mathematical measure for it?
How is it related to thermodynamical order and entropy?

These questions illustrate the modern form in which the riddle of life confronts us.

The present book represents an attempt to elucidate these problems from a new angle. But my aims are limited: I make *one fundamental assumption* and seek an answer to *one fundamental question*. My assumption is that, in abstraction, the living organism and its environment may be regarded as physical systems whose state at any time can in principle be specified in terms of physical variables. My question is— granted this assumption, is it possible to characterize the distinctive orderliness and directiveness of organic activities in terms of mathematical relations between these physical variables? In other words, can we construct mathematical concepts capable of characterizing the essential nature of biological organization?

In pursuing this goal I am not seeking mathematical precision for its own sake. I am fully aware that there are occasions in the development of science when a vague concept may prove more profitable than a precise one. Nor is it my intention to develop a new calculus where at present there may be nothing to calculate. I am merely acting on the conviction that here is a case which offers small prospects of progress unless we move to a higher level of precision in the choice of our concepts.

This is not to say that we shall find all the answers. The present book is no more than an experiment in the construction of new and precise concepts where the old and vague ones have failed us. Although I maintain that my analysis of the traditional biological concepts correctly covers their meaning within the limits set by the fluctuations of their actual usage, the new concepts which I shall advance on the strength of this analysis are defined merely tentatively. My main concern is to point the direction in which I distinctly see light. To go the whole way would require the labour of more than one man. Above all it would require the collaboration of men who are specialists in the various territories that would have to be traversed.

To avoid misunderstandings it must be stressed that I am merely concerned with the *characterization* of the directiveness of life processes and biological organization. Frequently this entitles me to make simplifications which I could ill afford were my object the discovery of new biological laws or of new mathematical techniques of prognostic value. For instance, one of the concepts we shall analyse is that of 'adaptation', and I shall attempt to characterize in mathematical terms the relationships which exist when something is said to be 'adapted' to something else. In doing so I shall assume, as I have said, that, in abstraction, both this 'something' and this 'something else' can in principle be specified in terms of physical variables. Now for the purposes of such characterization it is plainly irrelevant to ask exactly how many variables would be involved in those specifications at different levels of abstraction, or how their values would be determined in practice. Indeed, sometimes I shall proceed as if only one variable were involved in each case; and on one or two occasions[1] when no such representative variable lies readily at hand, I shall boldly invent one. In the given context I regard such simplifications as entirely justifiable, particularly if one bears in mind that from a mathematical point of view we can always treat a finite set of variables as a single variable whose value is determined by the constellation of the values of the members of the set.

One of the difficulties inherent in my aim was to find a method of exposition which would be as intelligible to the biologist who is no mathematician as to the mathematician who is no biologist, or the philosopher who is neither. At times this difficulty seemed insuperable, particularly if the difficulties of language were taken into account. The method finally adopted is a compromise in which the bare minimum is explained to enable the uninitiated to follow at least the essential steps in the argument. Thus the mathematical chapter is preceded by a verbal analysis and introduced by a section in which the most important elementary concepts are

[1] §§ 28 and 37.

briefly explained; at the same time the general level of abstraction is deliberately held as low as possible.

Many scientific subjects and methods other than those mentioned in the text had to be explored before the ones best suited to the purpose of this work could be selected, and my thanks are due to all those who helped in these preliminary studies, also to Prof. G. R. Ryle, Dr. J. Bronowski, and Mr. D. M. MacKay who were good enough to read the typescript. But I am particularly anxious to express my gratitude to Prof. P. B. Medawar, F.R.S.; I owe much to his constant encouragement, and his painstaking criticism of the first formulation of the main ideas developed in this book has enabled me to carry out valuable improvements in their exposition.

G. S.

OXFORD
May, 1950

CONTENTS

I

INTRODUCTION

§ 1. *What is Life? The Need of Critical Analysis*

AT the time of writing, scientific theory can show no unified body of thought which offers an explicit scientific formulation, critical analysis, and interpretation of the general nature of observed life, and which, strictly speaking, deserves to be called 'theoretical biology'. Modern biology has made immense strides in explaining the 'part events' of vital activities and the material matrix in which life functions, but it has failed to explain the *general* nature of observed life, and to enlighten the contemplative mind of Man about the place of life in the general scheme of things. Consequently, the influence of modern biology on Man's world-view has often been misleading rather than illuminating, and it has tended to foster immature forms of rationalism, some of whose repercussions have been world wide.

It is sometimes suggested that this failure of biology to deal with the general nature of life must be attributed to the far-going specialization of modern science and to the resulting inability of many scientists to see the wood for the trees. But the reason lies deeper. It must be seen mainly in the fact that biology has not so far been able to analyse and paraphrase in precise and exact scientific, i.e. physico-mathematical, terms, the really fundamental characteristics of observed life in the full and original meaning of that word: that *apparent pur-posiveness* and goal-directed character of vital activities which make the distinction between living and non-living systems in nature one of the most important distinctions Man draws among the objects of his environment: those characteristics of observed life which invite us to think of living things as somehow endowed with a soul, as somehow capable of personal relationship; those characteristics which invite us to think of living nature as permeated by intelligence and purpose, and whose loss we mourn when death occurs.

5235

B

A question of the type 'What is so-and-so?' may mean at least two very different things. On the one hand, 'so-and-so' may be an expression wholly unknown to us, which we wish to see defined intelligibly. 'What are diophantine equations?' we may ask. On the other hand, 'so-and-so' may be a term which is already common currency and of whose connotation we may have an adequate, although as yet quite intuitive and vague, grasp. We now ask, 'What is "so-and-so"?' in order to see this more or less intuitive knowledge crystallize into an explicit and articulate formulation which will enable us to realize its place in the general scheme of things. When Man's urge for knowledge and his desire to feel more at home in the universe, prompts the question 'What is life?' it is undoubtedly in this latter sense that the question is put. And if it is conceded that of the many functions of science the most important in the long run is to satisfy these desires, then we must admit that any biology which cannot answer the question 'What is life?' in this sense, fails in a vital part of its mission.

In biochemistry and biophysics, modern science has given the world an advanced analysis of the physical and chemical 'part events' occurring in animate matter, and throughout this book the principles and results of these sciences will be accepted without question. We shall also accept the conclusion to which their results point, viz. that we have every reason to believe all the events occurring within animate matter to be fully accountable for in terms of the laws of physics and chemistry.

But the progress of science has failed to supplement this advance by an equally critical analysis and scientific formulation of the objective phenomena and relations which constitute the observed fact of *animation* as such. And as long as we fail in explicitly formulating and analysing these really fundamental characteristics of observed life in exact scientific terms, no scientific explanation of life can be forthcoming. It is obvious that nothing can be scientifically explained unless it can first be explicitly formulated in scientific terms. The most detailed physical description of the raindrops and their attendant electro-magnetic fields, fails to be a scientific explanation of the rainbow as long as it fails to refer explicitly to the fundamental characteristics of the phenomenon, i.e. to the type of linear colour sequence which the word 'rainbow' connotes.

Similarly, the most detailed physical account and explanation of the events occurring within the boundaries of a living organism fails to be an account of life as such, so long as no explicit mention is made of the true characteristics of the organism as a whole. We are not dealing here with an unusual scientific case: it is widely known in the scientific world that the most important step towards the solution of a problem or explanation of a phenomenon is its exact formulation. The first step towards a theoretical biology, therefore, must be a critical analysis of the idea of life as such and an attempt on the strength of this analysis to find an exact formulation of the most truly distinguishing characteristics of life.

Broadly speaking we may distinguish three main groups of contemporary biologists.

The first and largest group is of those whose attitude towards the general nature of life is simply to point out physicochemical constituents and reactions which are typical of living organisms and to show how they might be accounted for by the laws of physics and chemistry, or how their origin can be explained in terms of modern evolutionary theory. Although this attitude yields scientific answers to many questions, it does not answer the main question at issue. The fundamental characteristics of life remain unformulated and unexplained. In a certain sense, this school of thought explains life away. Even if all concrete life processes could be traced down and explained, to the movement of the last electrons involved and the last resonance effects between them, we should have advanced no further towards a solution of the general riddle of life. The mistake of this school of thought is that it explores the denotation of life in terms of existing physical and chemical concepts instead of its connotation with the aid of new concepts. Some adherents have gone so far as to assert that since on these lines no satisfactory distinction between living and non-living systems can be found, the terms 'life' and 'living' must be regarded as meaningless as far as the exact sciences are concerned. This, of course, is a counsel of despair. The fact that scientists have so far proved unable to paraphrase the meaning of life in exact scientific terms, should not lead them to abandon the concept as meaningless, but rather urge them to double their efforts. Any other course of action reduces biology to an ultimate irrelevancy. The riddle of life is not solved by abolishing life.

The second group of biologists abandons *faute de mieux*, whenever it comes to the general problem of life, the canons of exact scientific thought, and descends to the vague language of philosophical speculation. Thus we get explanations of life in such vague and unscientific terms as the 'emergence of a new type of order', 'psychic' or 'hormic' forces, 'wholes which are more than the sum of their parts' and other vague phrases. No matter how sincere and profound these attempts at wider generalization may be, and no matter how valuable as expressions of personal insight, they cannot fail to disappoint the serious seeker after scientific truth. These are not scientific answers and their inclusion in scientific books is misleading. They are valuable only in their place, which is among the broad generalizations of speculative philosophy. But science has stolen the thunder of metaphysical speculation, and, having once breathed the pure air of exact scientific thought, the modern mind insists on scientific answers to its questions.

The third prominent group of biologists comprises those who are vaguely aware of the bankruptcy of both the above schools of thought, yet do not know how to break away, and in consequence fight shy of the general problem of life altogether. We thus witness the paradoxical situation to-day that the best biologists are often the most difficult scientists to interest in the riddle of life, and to convince that over and above the special problems on which they are engaged there still exists the one fundamental and general problem.

In order to find the solution of the general problem of life, biology must therefore make a fresh start. It must begin with a critical analysis of the idea of life as such and a determined attempt to paraphrase the connotation of that word in exact scientific terms, i.e. in terms of clearly defined spatio-temporal relationships between quantitative variables. In other words, theoretical biology must begin by being *analytical.* It is with the object of establishing such a new and analytical approach, and with a view to illustrating at once its possibilities and its power to add to our understanding of the general nature of life, that this book has been written.

§ 2. *The Apparent Purposiveness of Life Processes*

What are the fundamental characteristics of observed life in the sense of the preceding section? If we abandon scientific exactitude and provisionally attempt to express these fundamental characteristics of living systems in non-scientific and largely metaphorical language, we may say that they consist in the apparent purposiveness of vital activities and in the manner in which this apparent end-serving or goal-seeking quality integrates the part events of living systems into the self-regulating, self-maintaining, and self-reproducing organic wholes which we recognize as living individuals. That is to say, the distinguishing character of vital activities is their apparent subservience to biological needs which lie in the future, and to such fundamental biological ends as development, self-maintenance, or reproduction. Biological adaptation ('futurity adaptation' as some writers have called it), adaptive behaviour, physiological-, behavioural-, or morphological regulation, nervous and muscular ('anticipatory') coordination— are outstanding examples of vital activities which have this end-serving character. It is the all-pervasive presence of this apparent purposiveness in life processes, and the resulting possibility of thinking of living systems in terms of the 'goals' towards which their activities are directed, which is mainly responsible for the radical difference between the ways we think about living and non-living things.

How characteristic and pervasive a feature of vital activities this purpose-like character is, only those can fully appreciate who are able to survey the whole realm of biological phenomena. With the possible exception of that fringe of creatures which the conventional denotation of the word 'life' assigns to the borderline between the organic and inorganic world, it would be hard to find any level of organic activity which does not invite us to think of vital activities as being somehow purposive, as being subject to tendencies which are directed towards the fulfilment of specific and mutually inter-related ends. On the phenomenal level from which all science must proceed, life is nothing if not just this manifestation of apparent purposiveness and organic order in material systems. In the last analysis, the beast is not distinguishable from its dung save by the end-serving and integrating activities which unite it into an ordered, self-regulating, and single whole, and impart to the individual whole that unique independence from the vicissitudes of the environment and that unique power to hold its own by making internal adjustments, which all living organisms possess in some degree. It is this purpose-like subordination of the parts to the whole which, as Claude Bernard wrote, makes of the complex creature a connected system, a whole, an individual.

In other words, the failure of science to analyse and inter-pret the fundamental characteristics of life, is caused by its failure to analyse and interpret in exact scientific terms the nature of this purposelike character of life processes. The first task of analytical biology, therefore, must be to tackle this problem, and, without loss of scientific precision, to distil from the modern physico-chemical description of living nature that element of apparent purposiveness and organic order which nature parades so patently in all its organic manifestations, and which so far has appeared instantly to dissolve at the touch of scientific concepts. To put it naïvely, the fundamental problem of theoretical biology is to discover how the behaviour of myriads of blind, stupid, and by inclination chaotic, atoms can obey the laws of physics and chemistry, and at the same time become integrated into organic wholes and into activities of such purpose-like character.

It is not difficult to see why exact science has been unable to cope with this purposive or goal-directed aspect of organic nature: science still lacks really exact concepts in terms of which it can even as much as describe it, let alone interpret it. Biologists have been too keen to explain things before they were able to state in exact terms what they wanted to explain and what objective system-properties they were studying. Instead of scientific theories about the exact spatio-temporal relations and types of order involved in the organization of living systems, we find but hazy descriptions of the various purposive aspects of life in terms of such vague and often anthropocentric concepts as 'adaptation', 'subservience', 'coordination', 'regulation', 'integration', 'organization', 'final causation', &c., none of which, as they stand, attain to that standard of exactness which modern mathematical theory has shown to be indispensable to a strict and deductive scientific system. The result is a welter of discordant opinions about the general nature of life, and that typical inability to reach agreement, which so often accompanies the use of philosophical concepts whose inherent vagueness allows of almost as many readings as there may chance to be readers. None of these traditional biological concepts tell us much more than that there is in nature something analogous to the purposive behaviour of Man; but what this is biologists have so far been unable to say with precision. It is the main task of our analytical biology to remedy this failure.

Questions concerning the intrinsic meaning of the purpose-like quality of organic activities, and of the characteristic order found in living nature, have long been stock questions in the philosophy of life. In particular the relation of this apparent purposiveness to the determinism of classical physics has been the focus of many philosophical disputes. It is a commonplace that, ever since Descartes forged his rigid separation between mind and matter, the world has been struggling without success to bring the two together again. And the sterile controversy in biology between the scientists who postulated the existence of mysterious psychic agents or

directive forces in the organism to account for its purposiveness, and the mechanists who treated the organism as little
more than a complicated machine, is but a reflection of this
struggle. In the main stream of Greek thought there was no
room for such controversy. The essence of an organism was
identified with its 'form', i.e. with the principle of its organization, and nature was a single, organic, and striving whole. In
few branches of philosophy have discordances of opinion been
of greater detriment to the sanity of Man's world-view than
these. But for these discordances it would hardly have seemed
possible for the adherents of the conflicting viewpoints which
divide East and West to-day, to entrench themselves so uncom-
promisingly behind the alleged primacy of matter on the one
hand and of the spirit on the other. The result of our work
will, I hope, throw new light on these philosophical questions
and will perhaps advance some distance towards reuniting
mind and matter. Meanwhile the only safe conclusion to be
drawn from the persistence and dogmatic temper of these
controversies is that the philosophical concepts in terms of
which they are conducted are too vague to allow the formulation of conclusive arguments. Quine once said that the less a
science is advanced, the more does its terminology tend to rest
on the uncritical assumption of mutual understanding. In the
philosophy of life this uncritical assumption has obviously
proved unjustified. New concepts, new rigour and precision
are required.

This means that the critical analysis of life which was
demanded above must go hand in hand with a determined
effort to construct new and precise concepts, adequate to
replace the traditional ones without loss of meaning, thus
enabling the discussion to be raised to the required level of
precision. The logical and linguistic structure of such traditional concepts as 'adaptation', 'integration', 'organization', &c., must be exposed and then paraphrased in exact
scientific terms. We must, in effect, discover how to express
the concerns of the vitalists in the exact scientific language of
the mechanists. Carnap has adopted the term '*explication*' for

the process of giving an old and vague concept a precise and more explicit meaning. In this technical sense the term has since gained widespread currency, and we shall use it throughout this work. He calls the old and the new concept the 'explicandum' and the 'explicatum' respectively. In this terminology, therefore, we may say that the primary task of our analytical biology is to present the biologist with suitable scientific explications of the vague concepts which we are accustomed to use for describing the general nature of life.

This process of explication is not unlike the early analysis and refinement which the concepts of mechanics had to undergo before this branch of natural philosophy could become the exact theoretical science which it is to-day. From a theoretical point of view, biology is still in a pre-Galilean stage, and the early history of mechanics illustrates well the procedure we have to adopt. In those early days scientists disputed about the 'power', 'resistance', 'magnitude', and 'efficacy' of motions in much the same vague way in which we to-day talk about the 'adaptiveness', 'purposiveness', and 'integration' of organic behaviour. And their discussions were as inconclusive. Only when a precise mathematical definition had been found for the 'magnitude of motion'; only when the single concept of 'resistance' was replaced by the mathematical concepts of 'inertia' and of 'resisting forces'; only when d'Alembert's mathematics had shown the dispute between the Leibnizians and Cartesians on the efficacy of motion to be a mere dispute about words; only when 'mass' and 'power' had been replaced by adequate mathematical concepts—only then could theoretical mechanics come to full fruition, and could physicists reach a constructive measure of agreement on questions which had previously issued merely in a plethora of discordant philosophical speculations.

The main difficulty which besets the metaphorical concepts we are accustomed to use in a description of the purposiveness of vital activities and organic order, is that they imply a reference to some future goal towards which the respective organic activity is directed, and that this reference seems to be an essential and unalienable part of their meaning. They are, to say the least, quasi-teleological. When we say that the behaviour of an animal is 'adapted' to a given environment, we mean that it is so adapted from the point of view of some hypothetical goal towards the attainment of which we conceive this behaviour to be directed. It may be a proximate goal, as when an animal captures its prey, or an ultimate goal such as the survival of the individual or of the species. All the other concepts which we have mentioned in this connexion, such as 'coordination', 'co-operation', 'regulation', 'integration', 'organization', have the same finalistic reference.

It is impossible to deprive these concepts of their reference to the future without doing violence to their essential meaning. A good example of the emasculation which any of them may suffer from such treatment may be seen in the meaning which the concept of 'adaptation' has acquired in the hands of some mechanists. Deprived of its implicit reference to the future, the statement that an animal is adapted to its environment, becomes no more than a trivial affirmation that both the animal and the environment exist, and that the former is alive in the latter. It is this essential reference to the future which is responsible for all the confusion that has surrounded these concepts, and which, of course, is the main bone of contention between vitalists and mechanists.

The various ways in which the vitalists have dealt with this reference to the future are well known. The impossibility of incorporating their vague teleological concepts into a strictly scientific description of nature proved fatal. To-day it is fairly common ground among scientists that living nature is not teleological in the sense of employing anything akin to 'finalistic causation', and the attempts of vitalists to account for the apparent purposiveness of vital activities by invoking mysterious 'purposive agents', 'vital forces', 'entelechies', or other non-material components alleged to be present in living matter, have faded out of the main currents of biological thought. The interpretation of the process of organic 'becoming', in terms of the 'potential' or 'future' purposively forcing its way into the 'actual' or 'present' in the manner of such finalistic causation, has already come to be regarded as not merely scientifically sterile, but, in concrete scientific terms, an absurdity. These, however, are details of a dead controversy.

The mechanists were undoubtedly right in rejecting the teleology of the vitalists as scientifically sterile and as making nonsense of physical science. Yet they undid all they had gained by failing to realize that the unique manner in which vital phenomena appear to be tailored to the application of teleological concepts and positively invite their use, points to very real differences between animate and inanimate matter—differences whose objective foundation in some kind of spatio-temporal relationships it seems hardly possible to deny, even though we may not know what exactly these spatio-temporal relationships are. They also failed to realize that it should be the first task of biology to unmask these relationships.

Consider a concrete example. If we say that we 'try' to catch a fly, we regard this as a perfectly legitimate use of the verb 'to try'. But if we next say that the fly in the hollow of our hand will 'try' to escape, our modern scientific training intervenes and warns us that in the second case we are committing an illicit anthropomorphism. The fly, we are warned, is not a conscious rational agent, and therefore does not in any literal sense 'try' anything. This rigour of thought is very laudable. Yet in spite of these wise injunctions the incontrovertible fact surely remains that there is a unique something about the observed behaviour of the fly which quite emphatically invites this anthropomorphism and which renders this behaviour far better suited to such an analogy and teleological conception than, say, the behaviour of a falling stone.

What is this elusive something? What is its foundation in the objective realm of spatio-temporal relationships and functional interdependences between material events? How can it be scientifically defined and analysed? How can it be extracted from the physical description of the fly's behaviour? That, in a sense, is the crucial question. It is inconceivable that this goal-directed character of observed life should lack an underlying physical reality. At the same time it is a question which the vitalists have most persistently muddled and the organicists begged, while the mechanists have preferred the devil of scepticism to the deep sea of vagueness.

The doctrine that there is no place in exact science for a distinction between living and non-living systems, is often based on the argument that in the light of modern knowledge we can arrange known systems into a continuous sequence which passes without interruption, and unobtrusively, from obviously living systems to the obviously non-living. Any scientific distinction between life and the lifeless, therefore, could do no more than draw an arbitrary line across such an intrinsically continuous ladder of being. This argument ignores the fact that the obviously living systems are characterized by a distinct and unique behaviour of a kind that renders it of the greatest practical and theoretical importance to distinguish them by our terminology. The observation that different material systems display these purpose-like and organizational characteristics in varying degrees and some in doubtful degrees, seems hardly relevant to the desirability of using a nomenclature and dichotomy which recognizes their occurrence and significance. One would hardly consider influenza an unworthy subject for scientific study, or a scientifically superfluous concept, on the grounds that some people may contract it in doubtful degrees.

§ 3. *Vital Organization and Analytical Biology*

The ground lost by the vitalists in recent generations was only in part gained by the mechanists. Vitalism was not without heirs, at least temperamentally: men who rightly remained puzzled by the apparent purposiveness shown by the behaviour of living matter and who continued to recognize this to be the real hard core of the riddle of life.

They advanced beyond vitalism in recognizing that the cause of the purpose-like behaviour of living systems lies in the presence of special organizational relationships. Thus the emphasis shifted to the concept of *organization*, and a number of schools of thought developed around this concept. Emergencism, holism, and organicism are probably the best-known philosophical currents in this stream of thought. In the view of these writers a living organism is distinguished from inorganic matter by a higher level of organization.

But none of these schools manage to tell us in precise scientific terms what exactly is meant by 'organization' and what exact spatio-temporal relationships distinguish a higher form of organization from a lower. Their philosophical speculations are as vague and obscure as those of their predecessors.

A related but, on the whole, sounder line of thought was followed by those biologists who accepted the concepts of 'organization' and 'levels of organization' as capable of expressing the fundamental and distinguishing characteristics of observed life, but who also realized that the mere introduction of these concepts did not as such provide an answer to the problem of life. Their persistent cry that the central problem of biology was the problem of biological organization no doubt pointed in the right direction and did service to biology even if they had no other contribution to make. For while the concept of 'organization' keeps the purpose-like character of vital processes continuously before our eyes (since it is only through the apparent purposiveness of the activities to which they give rise that the existence of higher levels of organization can be detected), it yet implies that the purpose-like character of life processes has a foundation in objective spatio-temporal relationships. And, hence, it implies the possibility that some day it may prove possible to express—as indeed our analysis will attempt to do—the really fundamental character of life in exact scientific terms, and to incorporate it in a single and consistent scientific picture of the universe. In this sense the modern emphasis on organization has no doubt paved the way for the analytical approach which we are about to undertake.

To sum up. The main aim of our analytical approach to the study of life is to form a set of deductively employable concepts which will enable theoretical biology to deal with the really fundamental characteristics of observed life, viz. its apparent purposiveness. In order to achieve this aim we shall

(*a*) analyse the characteristic purposiveness of life-processes and clarify the spatio-temporal relations which underlie it;

(*b*) show how the results of this analysis may be formulated in terms of exact mathematical relations between quantitative variables, thus exposing the objective foundation which the apparent purposiveness of life has in the universe of physics;

(*c*) use these results to replace by accurate scientific concepts the vague concepts biologists and philosophers are accustomed to employ in the description of the purposiveness of natural events;

(*d*) show how this increased precision of thought may serve to throw new light on many features of life which were hitherto understood only imperfectly; and

(*e*) indicate some of the theoretical consequences which follow from our demonstration that the purposiveness of natural events has an objective basis in time and space, and may in fact be regarded as a *physical* property, as real and genuine as any property of matter studied by modern physics.

§ 4. *Outlines of the Factual Background*

For the benefit of the non-biologist and for those who like to inspect the factual background before embarking on a theoretical discussion, I shall give a short sketch of the ways in which the purposiveness of vital activities and biological order manifests itself most markedly. Biological adaptation, regulation, coordination, co-operation, and integration are some of the outstanding phenomena we shall have to deal with, and the following pages may serve to illustrate these and others in turn.

Biologists most often speak of *adaptation* if a living organism undergoes changes which appear to serve its survival. Changes of this type may either accompany the evolution of a species or the development of a single organism and we speak of 'phylogenetic' and 'ontogenetic' adaptations accordingly. However, it is also customary to speak of end-serving behaviour as 'adaptive' behaviour. The 'end' of adaptive changes or adaptive behaviour need not necessarily be the ultimate survival of the organism or of the species, but may be a more proximate condition which in certain cases may bear no relation to the organism's survival, and may even be detrimental to it. When a monkey grabs a fruit, this is called an adaptive movement irrespective of whether the fruit is wholesome or poisonous. Again, the movement of panic-stricken animals which are about to rush to their certain death in a forest fire, may just as properly be described as adapted to the obstacles in their path as when the animals are running to safety.

An instance of other important facts to be borne in mind in any attempt to grasp in full what adaptation means, is this: If a chameleon changes its colour in the normal way to match the shade of its environment, we call that an instance of adaptive behaviour, but if it happens to fall into a pot with the right colour of paint we would not seriously call that adaptive behaviour. I say this merely to put the reader on his guard and to dispel at once any facile optimism that the concept of adaptation is a simple one, or empty of real problems.

The impact of modern learning and education on the development of the adolescent often leaves a young student with a strangely confused attitude towards the many adaptations in nature which strike his eye. His first conscious awareness of phylogenetic adaptations concerns the relation between form and function. In observing the innumerable morphological adaptations of our flora and fauna, the child makes his first acquaintance with the solutions nature has found for the engineering problems which different forms of existence raise: the streamlined fish, the winged bird, the long-necked giraffe, and many others. Later his imagination is stirred by the intricate and ingenious arrangements of our garden plants for securing fertilization, preventing self-fertilization, and for the dispersal of their seed: the honey and scents with which they attract insects, the colours which guide these from afar, and the markings which serve as their further signposts. In the Calceolarias he fancies a saddle provided for the insect to sit on and he will recognize little stirrups in other flowers. He admires the spring-like action developed by Crucianella to shoot pollen at the insect, and the opening mechanism of the pea flower. Then there are the parachutes, slings, catapults, pepper pots, bristles, winged planes, and other contrivances used by our flowers to disperse their seed. In his botany lessons he studies the tropisms of young shoots and roots, the plant movements, the climbing devices, or even the manner in which Linaria bends back the stalk bearing the seeds after fertilization, twists around so that the faded flowers face the wall instead of the sun, and gradually pushes the seed into some cranny between the bricks.

Then again, the young naturalist marvels at the protective coloration found in the animal kingdom, the mimicry, or the advanced technique of counter-shading, ruptive markings, illusions of false relief, marginal shadows, &c. And he finds their appeal further enhanced when they are supported by matched patterns of behaviour. There are, for instance, the geometrid caterpillars which resemble little twigs and if disturbed take up correspondingly rigid positions, the innocuous insects which mimic some ferocious relative, the butterflies whose wings resemble withered leaves or copy the colour shades of flowers and grasses on which they rest, the moth which orients itself so that its markings coincide with the veins of the leaves on which it lives.

As his knowledge matures he comes to recognize the principle of the lever in the human arm, the principle of the pulley in the *obliquus superior* muscle of the eye, and much elementary physics in the climatic adaptations of leaf structure in plants.

But then arrives the day when he learns how most of these phenomena can be causally accounted for in terms of physics and chemistry, and the hit-and-miss of natural selection. The romance comes to a sudden end, his original wonder and sense of divine mystery suddenly find themselves opposed by authori-tative scientific voices telling him to regard all these pheno-mena as no more than the chance results of essentially blind physico-chemical forces, and as cosmologically insignificant. From a social and religious point of view a valuable attitude of mind is often lost thereby. Living nature ceases to be some-thing with which Man can enter into personal relationships.

Which of these opposing tendencies finally sways his thought and feeling will largely depend on his temperament and the influence of his teachers. But few, indeed, are those who can steer the middle course and emerge with a detached scientific attitude which realizes the importance of avoiding facile romanticism about the harmony and purposiveness of nature, and yet recognizes this purpose-like character of life and organic order to be immensely significant. Few are those who recognize these phenomena for what they are: a type of order which, in spite of all biophysical, biochemical, and genetical discoveries, has remained a challenge to clear thinking.

Instinctive behaviour provides another large store of con-spicuous phylogenetic adaptations. Their popular appeal has made many of these examples commonplace. The thoughts of every naturalist are provoked by the manner in which birds hatched from incubators instinctively know how to build their nests and assume their parental responsibilities. Even more striking examples from the insect world also jump to the mind. In the instinctive behaviour of the social and other insects, it is particularly easy to allow striking examples such as that of the spinning ants, *Oecophylla smaragdina*,[1] to blind us to innumerable other, less spectacular, but no less intricate and significant patterns of coordinated activities. It is also easy to be provoked to romanticize. William Morton Wheeler recalls the beetle *Rhynchites betulae* which makes two transverse inci-sions into a birch leaf and folds the apical portions into a com-pact cone. These lines of incision have been shown to be mathematical curves of such a nature as to represent the

---

[1] Teams of which draw the edges of leaves together while their companions bind these together with silk spun by the larvae.

evolute of an evolvend and so to produce the leaf area precisely suited to the beetle's purpose. He cites the romantic
significance attached to this behaviour by Wasmann and
others who saw in this evidence of an intelligence which solved
these complicated mathematical problems millions of years
before the genius of Man discovered their solution. It is easy
to overlook how rigid and unadaptable such behaviour patterns may be, and they lose some of their emotional appeal
once this is realized. *Rhynchites betulae* may be able to draw the
evolute of an evolvend but, presumably, could not produce a
straight incision to save its life. On emerging from the ground
after hatching, the caterpillar of the butterfly *Porthesia
crysorrhoea* is strongly heliotropic and if it is placed in a jar
which contains food on one side but a strong light on the other
its stereotyped heliotropic behaviour prevents it from finding
the food even to the point of death through starvation.

In passing from such phylogenetically adapted but comparatively rigid behaviour patterns to the adaptive and
flexible responses which the organism currently makes to the
flux of environmental events, we enter a further large realm
of natural phenomena possessing a strongly purposive quality.
This ranges all the way from the literally purposive behaviour
of Man down to the simple activities of protozoa. For although
adaptability of behaviour exists far more extensively in the
higher forms of life than in the lower (and is in fact often used
as a criterion for this distinction), even the simplest tropisms
usually involve some small degree of adaptability.

Between phylogenetic modifications and the behaviour of
living adults stand the modifications which the individual
undergoes in the course of ontogenesis and in passing through
his life cycle. Even if we postpone for the moment the question
of embryonic development, it is easy to find numerous illustrations of ontogenetic adaptations which the living organism
undergoes in response to special demands made by the environment. Familiar examples are the enlargement of our striated
muscles in response to persistent external demands; or the
degree to which our epidermis can adapt itself to exceptional

and protracted mechanical demands by thickening and becoming resistent. Connective tissue and growing bones have similar adaptive powers.

Habituation and learning also involve ontogenetic adaptations. Habituation or 'acclimatization', as it is often called, is the more widespread of these phenomena in the animal world. Behavioural habituation is known to be present in such low forms as sea anemones, and physiological habituation is known even in the very lowest forms of life. Thus, paramecia and other protozoa can acclimatize within individual clones to increased salinity of their environment, and the power of bacteria to increase their resistivity to drug action has also recently attracted attention.

So far we have mainly touched upon adaptations in morphological and behavioural phenomena, which are often the ones most easily observed in the study of living nature. But behind these easily observable activities there lies a world of hidden chemical and physical events which modern physiology is only gradually revealing. These physiological events show modes of adaptation as characteristic as any of the others. Here, too, we have innumerable phylogenetic adaptations, such as, for instance, the adaptations of the animal metabolism to the normal diet of the species.

With these examples we may for the present leave our illustrations of the extensive range and diversity of adaptation and adaptability in vital activities. It must be remembered, however, that adaptability is never unlimited. It may be very extensive, as in the higher organisms and especially in Man, but no living organism has the power to cope with all the conceivable challenges of its environment. On the contrary, the environmental changes which are possible in the normal routine of events are often so limited that, as someone has put it, few animals have a chance to show how foolishly they would act under irregular circumstances.

The concept of *regulation* in its most common biological uses refers to activities which 'aim' at ensuring the constancy of some environmental or internal condition. The latter case is the more common, for it seems to be the rule that the possibility of an organism maintaining itself as a going concern is contingent on its power to maintain a certain constancy of its 'milieu interne'. The regulative responses by means of which the living organism meets and offsets any disturbance of this constancy again furnish typical examples of the apparent purposiveness of organic behaviour. This is as true for the lower as for the higher forms of life, although once more the latter show progressively greater powers of regulation.

The body fluids play an essential part in the organism's internal environment. The proper functioning of the body requires of many substances that they should be present in this fluid matrix in certain critical concentrations. Many physiological mechanisms serve the regulation of these concentrations. The great sensitivity required of some of these physiological regulations is shown by such facts as that a frog's heart is killed if fluids are sent through it which have an excess acidity corresponding to about one part by weight of hydrogen-ions to one billion parts of water. The delicacy of the actual regulative reactions is illustrated by the fact that purified pituitary hormone has been found to be appreciably active in concentrations of one part in 18,000 million. It is also interesting to note the different rapidities with which some of these regulations take place. In Man, nervous inexcitability following the passage of a nerve impulse is said to last normally for only about a millisecond; excess of carbon dioxide in the blood lasts for a few seconds; excess of bromide may last for weeks; and of lead for years.

Some of the mechanisms involved in physiological regulation may be comparatively simple, such as the disposal of excess water through the kidneys, or excess carbon dioxide from the blood through increased pulmonary activity. But the complete reorientation of feeling and behaviour and the psychological reorganization which a human being undergoes in extreme thirst, show how complex and comprehensive a mechanism the body may be able to mobilize in real need. The regulation of the blood's osmotic pressure and oxygen content, or of body

temperature, are other familiar examples, and a particularly
striking illustration of the self-regulating powers of the body
and their purpose-like character is the fact that in starvation,
when the body proteins have to be broken down, the body will
break them down in the reversed order of their physiological
importance, so that the most vital tissues will be preserved
longest.

It would be wrong to give the impression that these regulative mechanisms are separate and isolated functional units,
each with its separate task. Many organs serve a variety of
functions. The liver is a good case in point. Conversely, there
often exists more than one mechanism to deal with any one
type of regulation. For instance, in regulating its temperature
the body makes use of such diverse mechanisms as the relaxa-
tion or constriction of peripheral blood-vessels, sweating,
panting, shivering, or adrenalin secretion.

In surveying these cases of internal regulation it must not
be forgotten that many animals also possess extensive powers
of regulating their external environment. Nearly every animal
at some stage of its life possesses motility and during this
period it can regulate its environment by migration or otherwise. In some cases, as in Man, the animal has the power to
regulate conditions in its environment not only by selection but
also by direct modifications.

Embryological processes show very wide powers of regulation. Here, to quote Needham,[1] the concept of regulation
denotes 'the extensive power embryonic forms of life have
to continue a normal or approximately normal development
or regeneration in spite of experimental interference by abla-
tion, addition (implantation), exchange (transplantation),
fusion, etc.'. And he adds: 'The processes thus revealed operate
in all embryos to a greater or lesser extent and may be regarded
as part of the sum total of processes whereby the organism is
rendered more or less independent of its environment.' It has
been shown that the cells of the blastulae of some animals, for
instance sea urchins, may be completely separated even up to

---

[1] *Biochemistry and Morphogenesis*, Cambridge, 1942.

the thirty-two-cell stage and yet each of these fragments will eventually give rise to a complete individual. Far-going transplantations of tissue can be carried out in young embryos without affecting the outcome of the embryonic development. In the case of the amphibian embryo, Spemann showed that, before gastrulation has begun, nearly all parts of the embryo are interchangeable with other parts without preventing the development of a complete and viable animal.

Remarkable, too, is the extensive regulation which regenerative processes may display. The regeneration of amphibian limbs, for instance, has been studied extensively alongside amphibian embryology. The amputated leg stump in adult newts can reorganize any mass of competent tissue grafted on to it, and regenerate a complete limb from it. But we must not let these spectacular examples and others, such as the power of any of a dozen fragments into which a flat-worm may be cut to regenerate a complete individual, or of a single Begonia leaf to regenerate an entire plant, cast into the shade the extensive powers of regeneration possessed by most living organisms from the single cell upwards. For instance, although Man's power of regeneration is more limited than in some lower forms of life, very extensive regulation and reorganization is nevertheless involved in the processes of wound healing or the repair of fractured bones. In both cases a large number of the cells involved come to assume new functions and undergo a considerable internal reorganization. Other striking examples of purpose-like activity in repairing organic injuries are the adjustments which higher organisms can make to interferences with their nervous system—although they have no power actually to replace destroyed nerve cells. The increased subtlety and discrimination which the human auditory faculties develop after loss of sight is a case in point. If the semicircular canals of a bird are injured, recovery is possible through a gradual substitution of optical impulses for the missing labyrinthine ones in maintaining postural control. In the transplantation of a nerve of the dog it has been claimed that functionally correct innervation takes place without any preceding incorrect movements. Similarly, in the transplantation of muscles it has been observed that the proper movement occurs immediately after removal of the bandage.

Closely akin, as far as its purpose-like character is concerned, is the fact of reconstitution as it is found in lower forms of life. The slime-mould, *Physarium polycephalum*, is not killed by being ground in a mortar with quartz sand and can pass without harm through soft and hard filter-paper. The Mycetozoa can 'creep' through cotton in fine strands which soon flow together again on the other side and form an organism having the same behaviour as before. In certain sponges, for instance, cells isolated by squeezing a part of the sponge through fine silk, will later reunite into little sponges.

Finally, mention must be made of another form of regulation which has a distinctly purpose-like quality. I mean the power of living organisms to create defensive substances in response to the entrance of foreign organic matter into vital parts of the system. The full extent of these immunological powers of living organisms are still imperfectly explored and little is known about the exact manner in which these foreign proteins or antigens are acted upon by the highly specific antibodies which the organism creates in its defence.

When a number of simultaneous organic activities which are not mutually dependent in any direct causal sense nevertheless seem to be directed to a single common goal—each proceeding, so to speak, as if it were aware of the others—or when they behave as if they were governed and dovetailed by a central, purposive, controlling agency, we are wont to speak of *coordinated* activities. The coordination of our voluntary muscles is an obvious example. A list of all the voluntary muscles or their antagonists which actively enter into a single human walking movement would be formidable indeed. The function of the central nervous system is, of course, primarily that of a coordinating organ. But coordinated animal and plant movements without the agency of any nervous system are also possible. For instance, the spiral movements of paramecia are due to a particular form of coordinated activity by its cilia.

The actual disengagement or dissociation of normally coordinated processes which can be brought about experimentally shows that coordination is a connective relationship which may allow considerable independence to the related parts. The experimenter can, for instance, secure the disengagement of growth from differentiation in embryonic tissues, nuclear division from cellular division, metabolism from either growth or differentiation.

A particularly wide field of coordinated activities is found in mutual co-operation and division of labour in higher animal associations. Insect societies have already been mentioned, and many additional examples could be chosen, ranging from the most primitive forms of family life to the complex co-ordinated activities of a modern nation at war.

Lastly, a word may be said about *integration*. Many of the purpose-like activities illustrated in this section are not, as such, necessarily exclusive properties of living organisms. In smaller measure they may be found in one form or another also in automata, servo-mechanisms, and other machines. An exclusive characteristic of life, however, is the way in which these purpose-like activities are dovetailed and unite the component parts or processes of living systems into actively self-maintaining, self-regulating, developing, and reproducing organic wholes—into living individuals. To denote this dovetailed mutual adjustment and collaboration of purpose-like activities the term 'biological integration' has gained widespread currency and we shall take it up in the same sense.

To express the differences in the degrees of integration, biologists often speak of different 'levels' of integration. It is largely according to these levels of integration that the biologist has come to form the idea of individual organic wholes possessing varying degrees of autonomy, and has come to speak, for instance, of 'cellular', 'metameric', and 'social aggregates'. The higher the level of integration of an organic whole, the greater, obviously, the suppression of local independence. In the lower multicellular organisms we find a very considerable independence of the parts. The beheaded earthworm will exhibit most of the responses of the intact animal except, for instance, the burrowing reaction. Associations of multicellular organisms also show varying degrees of integration. From mere aggregations which are held together by tropistic or sensory responses, and loose-knit food associations or biocoenoses, we ascend the scale to reproductive associations and families, to the large assertive associations of flocks and herds, thence to insect societies, to the societies of monkeys and apes, and finally, to the complex fabric of human societies. All these show conspicuous organizational relationships, and, alive to more subtle forms of organization, some biologists have not hesitated to extend the idea of an organic whole to include the entire realm of living nature. Such conceptions are often based on the reciprocal nutritional dependence of the animal kingdom and the plant kingdom. Sometimes also they are based on the comparatively stable balance which nature keeps between different animal or plant populations. References to such facts as that cholera bacilli may divide every twenty minutes and that, therefore, each bacillus could in theory generate 7,366 tons of bacilli per day, are obviously misconceived and irrelevant. But it is true that an extensive increase in any one animal population may bring about a series of checks which bear some analogy to the self-regulating powers within individual organisms.

§ 5. *The Language of the Physical Sciences*

The main subject-matter of this book is the purposiveness of life processes and the manner in which this integrates living systems into organic wholes, for we have recognized these to be the fundamental characteristics of observed life. In the preceding sections these characteristics were discussed and illustrated in terms of such concepts as 'adaptation', 'regulation', 'coordination', 'integration', &c., and the upshot of our general remarks was that a theoretical biology cannot be born until these concepts can be translated into the physico-mathematical language of exact science, i.e. into clearly definable spatio-temporal relationships between quantitative variables. A fresh and primarily analytical start must be made.

This statement of our aims may have stirred up a number of the reader's prejudices. Words like 'adaptation', 'regulation', 'coordination', 'purpose', are good plain English words, and the reader may feel that nothing can be gained by any attempt to paraphrase them in a physico-mathematical language. Nothing can be clearer, they may say, than good plain English. Other readers may be put out by the very mention of mathematics in this context, for it may bring to their minds those many mathematical efforts in biology which can be considered as little more than fanciful and sterile titivations unrelated to the real problems biologists want solved.

These objections could be met simply by a plea to await the results of our method in the later parts of the book. The new light which these results shed on the general nature of life, will no doubt dispel hastily formed prejudices. Yet, it will not lead us too far astray if we briefly deal with one or two of these prejudices forthwith.

In the first place, it is important to recognize that while such plain English words as 'adaptation', 'purposiveness', &c., are good enough for ordinary discourse and for those simple deductive arguments to whose conclusions we can at any time apply an intuitive and commonsense check, they are far too vague for intricate deductive arguments, and for an elaborate logical theory or axiomatic system (e.g. for discovering whether two axioms are consistent). The concept system of the physical sciences and the language of physics is the most advanced system of thought and symbols which the human mind has been able to develop for the interpretation of nature. The physical sciences owe their immense success primarily to the manner in which their mathematical language has overcome the intrinsic shortcomings of the natural languages for difficult informative and theoretical purposes.

Secondly, modern physical science has developed an

immensely advanced and comprehensive picture of the universe in terms of mathematical relations between quantitative variables, and until we can translate the fundamental characteristics of observed life into that language we cannot bring the general phenomenon of life into a logical relation with the theoretical framework of modern physics, and incorporate it in a single comprehensive picture of the world. Nor can we rigorously examine such special issues as the compatibility of the purpose-like character of vital activities with the causal principles of macroscopic determinism upheld by modern physics.

Finally, such mathematics as we shall use will extend no further in relation to living organisms than (a) to treat the organism as a physical system, i.e. as a material system whose current state is in principle specifiable by means of quantitative parameters; (b) to employ the idea of one-one correspondences or functional relationships between certain sets of values of such parameters; (c) to use the customary mathematical symbols for such functional relationships, and (d) to use the idea of the derivative of a function, i.e. of the rate at which a change in one of a number of dependent parameters is accompanied by a change in one of the others. Moreover, these mathematical ideas will be used only qualitatively, i.e. for the purposes of introducing an indispensable degree of precision into our thoughts and symbols, and not for computative or prognostic purposes.

The main problem of any advanced informative language, particularly of any scientific use of language, is to find expressions and statements concerning whose meaning it is intrinsically possible to establish universal agreement and uniformity of interpretation among scientists. Men communicate with one another by means of conventional signs which can never mean quite the same to those who use them. The power of the scientific language lies in the degree to which it has succeeded in overcoming this inherent weakness, and in avoiding ambiguity or vagueness. This has made possible a measure of agreement among scientists about the facts they study and about possible interpretations for them which is unparalleled in any branch of human knowledge. Moreover, without this possibility of agreement and uniformity in interpreting the signs used the pooling of information and the scientific collaboration which is at the back of modern technical progress would have been unthinkable.

One reason for this need to avoid ambiguity and vagueness is that agreement about the meaning of a statement is an obvious prerequisite for agreement about its truth. Most scientific propositions are universal propositions and can, strictly speaking, never be more than tentatively accepted hypotheses. For no universal proposition can be strictly verified. Yet, agreement about the meaning of an hypothesis must obviously precede any agreement about its acceptability or about the question whether any particular experiment confirms of falsifies it.

But for the purpose of theory construction the most important reason why the informative use of language is vitiated by ambiguity or vagueness, is that ambiguous or vague meanings can invalidate any formal process of deduction and thereby make any deductive system of thought or theory impossible. It is well known that the classical syllogism may lead from correct premises to false conclusions if the verbal identity of the middle term fails to be accompanied by the real identity of the objects denoted in the two contexts, i.e. if the middle term is used ambiguously. To illustrate the mischief which the existence of a single ambiguity can do in a reasoned argument, a simple example may be cited which some readers may remember from their schooldays. Assume that in trying to define a certain expression, say the expression 'pure quantity', someone makes it clear that he means this expression to denote finite real numbers, but leaves it open whether or not this is to include the number zero. Under these assumptions the premiss that any 'pure quantity' is divisible by any other 'pure quantity'—which would be true if zero is excluded—allows us to arrive by simple mathematical reasoning (which assumes, however, zero to be included) to arrive at the conclusion that

$1 = 2$ and hence that any 'pure quantity' is equal to any other.[1]

This power of even so (*prima facie*) insignificant an ambiguity to lead to an infinite number of absurd or conflicting conclusions, is the bane of speculative philosophy. It is one of the main reasons why speculative philosophy has failed to interpret any aspect of reality in terms of a deductive system of thought on which a significant amount of agreement could be reached by philosophers. It is also the reason why instead of one comprehensive theory of life we have to-day but a collection of discordant and inconclusive philosophies of life, and why the best part of our efforts must go towards achieving real exactitude in the discussion of the fundamental characteristics of life. Only against this background of language and the intrinsic difficulties of its informative use can we come to see the physical sciences and the physico-mathematical language in their true perspectives.

To appreciate how the physical sciences have overcome these difficulties, it is necessary to distinguish between the two main sources of ambiguity or vagueness which exist in the informative use of language.

The first source of possible ambiguity or vagueness lies in the reference which the words or symbols used have to the world of perception, i.e. to the objects which they are meant to denote. Of any word or symbol which refers to the world of perception, the speaker must be able to make it absolutely clear what exactly the word refers to.

The second source of ambiguity or vagueness concerns the formal structure of the speaker's statements and their mode of statement composition. We may distinguish these two types

---

[1] The 'proof' runs as follows:

Assume that a and b are two equal numbers; then

$$a = b$$
$$\therefore \quad ab = b^2$$
$$\therefore \quad ab - a^2 = b^2 - a^2$$
$$\therefore \quad a(b-a) = (b-a)(b+a)$$
$$\therefore \quad a = b+a$$
$$\therefore \quad a = a+a$$
$$\therefore \quad 1 = 2.$$

of possible ambiguity and vagueness by calling them 'semantic' and 'formal', respectively. Which is the more important? Which the more fatal to the informative use of language? The answer is that either can be fatal, but that semantic vagueness is by far the more dangerous because in the past Man has been far less critical of it than of the formal correctness of his propositions and inferences. Logicians have for over two thousand years devoted themselves to the formal aspects of language, but only in our own age are men slowly beginning to grow alive to the importance of semantic precision.

An instructive example to show how very important this semantic precision is, may be taken from the general relativity theory. A cornerstone of the theory is Einstein's recognition that even so familiar, and to all appearances innocent, a concept as that of 'simultaneity' proves too ambiguous and vague when we try to establish by means of measurements whether or not it is fulfilled by distant events. Hence, the strict discipline of physical theory demands the rejection of the concept in this context. How much vaguer than the concept of 'simultaneity' are the concepts in terms of which we are accustomed to think of the fundamental characteristics of life!

How does the language and method of the physicist overcome the twin dangers of formal and semantic vagueness or ambiguity? It overcomes the first by resorting for all purposes of intricate deduction to the rigorous and precise formalism of mathematics; and it overcomes the second, as we have just seen, by operating with only such concepts and only such mathematical expressions that any reference which these expressions are intended to have to the world of perception can, either directly or indirectly, be made publicly clear and definite by the specification of a set of practical procedures (viz. operations of experiment and measurement) in terms of which it can in principle be ascertained whether the empirical conditions denoted by these expressions are, or are not, fulfilled in any given case. These two methods are linked together by the concept of *number* which allows the results of measurements to be expressed in the symbols of mathematics and hence enables us to apply mathematical reasoning to recorded empirical observations.

It is important to realize the fact that the only final way of making definite the meaning of any symbolic expressions which refer to the world of perception, and of securing uniformity of interpretation of such expressions, is by giving them so-called 'demonstrative definitions', i.e. by publicly demonstrating the objects or conditions which they are meant to denote. And the ultimate reason why operations of measurement can serve to give a definite meaning to a difficult physical concept is precisely that, since they consist of practical operations, they can be described entirely in terms of demonstratively definable expressions. If, for instance, the physicist is asked what exactly he means by the 'temperature' of a water-bath, he can make his exact meaning publicly clear by saying 'I mean the number indicated by a thermometer of such and such a construction and calibrated in such and such a way, when it is immersed in the water', and all the terms involved in this specification which have any reference at all to the world of perception, are in the last resort definable demonstratively. Alternatively, of course, he may give a merely formal thermodynamical definition of temperature, but in that case the concepts in terms of which he gives his definition admit—again either directly or indirectly by means of a further reduction—of being given a definite and public definition in terms of practical laboratory operations and measurements. It is true that in physical measurements it may not always be possible to reach agreement on the exact reading of a given instrument pointer, but it is as a rule possible to reach complete agreement on the limits between which its true reading lies, and since this margin of possible error can be formally taken account of in the mathematical evaluation of a given measurement, this difficulty is irrelevant in the present context.

In pure mathematics and symbolic logic a similar situation prevails. The rules according to which mathematical expressions may be formed and transformed (as in adding, sub-tracting, &c.) can be made clear in a public way by the simple act of demonstrating them on a piece of paper. Similarly, the rules for the combination and transformation of the signs used in modern logic can be made public and clear by—as Bridgman has put it—'demonstrable paper and pencil operations'.

In short, the secret of the success of the physical language in the description and interpretation of nature lies in the degree to which it eliminates the intrinsic vagueness of the natural languages by using demonstratively definable laboratory operations (viz. experiments and measurements) to correlate the facts of experience with a set of formal elements (viz. numbers), whose permissible combinations and transformations (adding, subtracting, &c.) are also publicly definable.

It is sometimes said that the secret of the physicist's success lies in the ultimate 'testability' of his propositions. In a certain sense this is merely another way of stating what we have already said, but I think it misleads by emphasizing a deriva-tive rather than a primary aspect of the matter. Before a proposition can be tested it must first be accepted as a signi-ficant hypothesis, i.e. we must be clear about its meaning.

Avoiding vagueness or ambiguity in scientific concepts must not be confused with avoiding elasticity of such concepts. While vagueness must be condemned, elasticity may yet be highly desirable. The use of a concept is elastic if its users remain prepared in the light of experience to consider alterna-tive definitions for it, and to revise its precise meaning. In the early stages of a scientific theory the existence of such elas-ticity may be of considerable importance. As long as the alternative definitions are sufficiently precise there is no contradiction between the elimination of vagueness and the maintenance of elasticity in the use of a concept. The ideas of 'number' in mathematics and of 'temperature' in physics are good examples in which precision was combined with elasticity in the course of their historical development. And in the development of suitable new concepts to deal with the phenomena of biological order we shall also endeavour to combine a minimum of vagueness with a maximum of elasticity. The concepts in terms of which Man chooses to think about the real world are the only things over which he has absolute power. He can make and unmake them. There is no such thing as the 'real' meaning of a concept to which its use has to conform. Although Man has, of course, 'real' habits and conventions of using certain words in certain ways, which it would be foolish to disregard in defining a word.

The superiority of physics in the realm of empirical thought is often loosely dismissed with a phrase to the ultimate effect that the world is made out of three types of elements: measurable quantities such as weight and temperature: unmeasurable quantities such as utility, desire, adaptation, organization, and qualities such as beauty; and it is said that physics has, as it were, an unfair advantage over the other sciences by confining itself to the study of the first type of element only. This mode of thought is very misleading. It is a serious confusion to project this threefold distinction into the objective world whereas it properly belongs only to the definiteness and precision of the concepts we use in thinking about that world. It is wrong to regard physics as a science whose subject-matter is objectively limited in this way. We must look upon physics as a science with an unlimited subject-matter but with a definitely limited conceptual apparatus, viz. one which is confined to concepts rigorously satisfying the strict formal and semantic requirements outlined above. It is important to realize this clearly, for unless we appreciate that the physico-mathematical system of to-day is not merely a set of propositions developed about an intrinsically limited aspect of nature, but a body of thought whose only limitation is the strict discipline imposed upon the choice of its concepts and upon the structure of its propositions, we may fail to see why it is both possible and desirable to extend this physico-mathematical discipline to other fields—such as in this case to the phenomena of biological order and organization. The distinguishing features of the physical sciences are not impressed upon them by their material, but by ideals of clear thinking.

Many important questions still lie well beyond the scope of physical thought, and speculative philosophy has this in common with all other bodies of theoretical thought which fail to satisfy the standards of precision achieved by modern physics, that it recognizes the power of language to convey, although not literal truth, at least some form of insight to suitable audiences. Thus it is prepared to discuss metaphorically and inconclusively rather than not at all the many important questions which physico-mathematical thought has so far been unable to reach. A. N. Whitehead's works are attempts to say significant things about the nature of organic order in such metaphorical terms. In some respects, indeed, he strains his metaphorical language almost to the limits of our associative faculties. No doubt such efforts are valuable, and their colourful phraseology contrasts strongly with the drabness of the physical language, but, however beautiful and masterly, such metaphorical systems of thought can never achieve the same conclusiveness and the same possibilities of agreement as scientific theories. There will always be as many conflicting philosophies as there are philosophers.

A clear distinction, therefore, can be drawn between physical theory and philosophy. The one sacrifices inclusiveness in the interest of conclusiveness, the other conclusiveness in the interest of inclusiveness. We need not on this account condemn either for its deficiencies. Our attitude towards them should be determined by the obvious recognition that the ideal must be the attainment of both inclusiveness and conclusiveness.

Finally, a word must be said about what is sometimes called the 'hypothetico-deductive' character of physical theory. This expression refers to the fact that the formal basis of physical theory, as of any theory in the empirical sciences, consists of interpreted axiom systems. An axiom system is a set of mutually consistent and very general formulae which are put forward without regard to any reference they may have to matters of fact and without regard to the question whether we can know them to be true or false, but solely on the ground that a certain larger collection of given and less general formulae can be deduced from them. An interpreted axiom system is one in which the collection of given formulae refer to matters of fact and consist of significant propositions which may be true or false. We are prepared to accept an interpreted axiom system as true if we can find no evidence that any consequences derivable from the axioms are false and know of some that they are true. Scientific theory attempts to explain empirical facts by developing suitable axiom systems and suitable rules for their interpretation. An empirical fact is 'explained' by a scientific theory if the propositions expressing it can be shown to be a consequence of the axioms of the theory. The foremost aim pursued in the development of any scientific theory is to find the simplest set of axioms which will enable all the observable phenomena studied by the branch of science concerned to be explained in this manner. For instance, in classical mechanics it was found that all the phenomena studied could be shown to be consequences of Lagrange's Equations of Motion. These equations were therefore accepted as a suitable set of axioms. Similarly, Maxwell's equations proved to be a suitable set of axioms for explaining the phenomena of electrodynamics.

The part played by induction in the development of scientific theory often tends to obscure this purely hypothetical character of the universal propositions of science and of the 'laws of nature' which science proclaims. Induction is a psychological process. It is a process in which we jump from the observation that this man was mortal and that man was mortal to the hypothesis that all men are mortal. The framing of an hypothesis is essentially a process of free invention; but when we pass from the observation of a very large number of men to the hypothesis that all men are mortal, this process of invention is, of course, a comparatively simple psychological step. When an hypothesis is based on induction it may derive special weight from our knowledge that it is *ipso facto* confirmed by a large number of test cases, but it still remains merely an hypothesis. Induction and deduction are therefore in all respects quite different. Deduction is a formal process in which one proposition is derived from another as a necessary consequence. It has logical compulsion. Induction, on the other hand, is a psychological process. It has, at best, psychological compulsion and can lead to falsehood as well as truth.

In the present volume we are only concerned with critical analysis and not with the construction of axiom systems. Nevertheless, the process of substituting new concepts for old ones is based on a process of free invention not unlike the invention of hypotheses, and the reader will fail to see this work in its proper methodological perspective unless he realizes the essentially hypothetical character of scientific theory.

PRELIMINARY ANALYSIS OF ADAPTATION

§ 6. *The Key Position of the Concept of Adaptation*

BEFORE proceeding to the technical explication of the purpose-like character of vital phenomena and of biological order, we shall begin with a preliminary analysis in terms of everyday concepts and without too much regard for technicalities, in order to discover in broad outline the spatio-temporal relationships with which these phenomena confront us. The next step will be to cast the results of this preliminary analysis into a precise physico-mathematical formulation.

Owing to the ambiguity and inherent vagueness of the concepts traditionally used to describe the purpose-like character of life processes, we must not expect from this preliminary analysis more than it is inherently able to give. We may indeed expect definite clues about the direction in which we have to search for precise concepts which are capable of paraphrasing and replacing the vague ones; but we must not expect our analysis to lead to the solution of our problem by a straight path of logical deduction. The vagueness of traditional biological concepts will at times inevitably confront us with a choice of meanings. In that case the principle of our choice should be clear: for the purposes of this work we must select those meanings which best seem to cover the really distinctive features of observed life.

We may begin by noting that the distinctive organizational features of living organisms confront us with some peculiar dependency of part on whole which cannot be apprehended except through the behaviour of the parts. In other words, the characteristics of organization and purposiveness are only perceptible in biological activity, and our first question, therefore, must concern the distinctive features of this activity. Nature is nature in action and no 'still' of life can convey the dynamic relationships in which the property of life resides.

Of the various concepts that suggest themselves in a description of the purpose-like character of vital phenomena, the more obvious have already been discussed and illustrated, e.g. 'adaptation', 'regulation', 'coordination', 'integration', &c. This is not to say that these concepts are mutually independent. Certainly the first three are closely interrelated and partly coextensive. Nevertheless, they are concepts of whose intelligibility we can be as tolerably satisfied as the present phase of discussion permits, and which do definitely penetrate to the core of life.

Now, an inspection of the examples given in § 4 reveals that in the last analysis these and related concepts describe no more than interlaced patterns of adaptive behaviour, however different they may at first sight appear to be. Their main differences lie merely in the degree of complexity to which they refer and in the nature of their 'goals', rather than in the presence or absence of new connective relationships. The fundamental relation, therefore, is that of *adaptation*. We may, indeed, regard this relation as the ultimate analytical element in all the other concepts, and any one of them could be adequately defined in terms of this relation. Evidently, we have here a key-concept in our present ways of thinking about the purpose-like aspects of nature.

On these grounds it is expedient to concentrate first of all on the analysis of the idea of adaptation; to discover whether there exist any objective spatio-temporal relationships in the living world to which this concept may be assumed significantly to refer; and to attempt to distil from these relations their elusive purpose-like character. The remainder of this chapter will be devoted mainly to this task.

§ 7. *The Concept of Appropriateness*

Speaking generally, it may be said that the notion of adaptation when applied to living nature refers to the widespread and striking *appropriateness* which organic activities show in relation to the needs of the organism, and to the *effectiveness* with which organisms meet the demands made upon them by their environment. For our present analytical purposes it will be expedient to take the idea of *appropriate response* as a starting-point and to begin by exposing some of the spatio-temporal relationships and patterns of causal connexions which it implies.

If we think of an organic response as a single, complex, physical event, the idea of appropriate response points beyond this complex event in three important respects.

In the first place, the response must be *to* something, it must be evoked or called into being by some antecedent environmental event or state of affairs.

Secondly, the response can be called 'appropriate' only in relation to the subsequent occurrence of some event or state of affairs towards the actual or probable occurrence of which we believe it to contribute effectively. This event or state of affairs is what is commonly regarded as the 'goal' or 'aim' of the response. Without explicit or implicit reference to this future event or state of affairs the idea of appropriateness is ambiguous, indeed meaningless. If a skater loses his balance, a response which would be appropriate from the point of view of restoring that balance would not necessarily be appropriate from the point of view of preserving the skater's dignity.

In most biological discussions this future event or state of affairs whose occurrence as the result of a given response is taken as the criterion for the response's appropriateness, consists of the subsequent survival of the given individual or of the species—or, at any rate, consists of the occurrence of some condition or event assumed to contribute to the probability of that survival. But it would be wrong to think that the idea of an appropriate response is confined to this particular case in biology. To recall an earlier example, even if a panicked animal happens to be running to its certain death we should still regard the action of jumping as an appropriate response to the approach of a given obstacle in its path. The response is now appropriate not from the point of view of the animal's survival but from the point of view of its continued movement along a certain path.

In the third place, whether or not a given response is appropriate depends on the environmental circumstances which it meets and with which it comes to interact. An action appropriate under one set of circumstances may be quite inappropriate under another. And the 'environmental circumstances' meant in this context are always circumstances which coincide with the execution of the response. They are circumstances which the response meets upon its execution and on which its success depends. Because, if under given environmental circumstances A an action B is said to be appropriate in respect of the successful realization of some subsequent environmental event C, the idea is: given A, the occurrence of C requires the occurrence of B. In other words, the occurrence of C is implied by the joint occurrence of A and B but not by the occurrence of either A or B alone. And unless A and B are here understood to refer to the same instant of time the possibility is left open for the occurrence of either one to imply the occurrence of the other and the whole conception would obviously become ambiguous and collapse. There is therefore a time lapse between the environmental conditions or events which initiate the given response and those on which its effectiveness is held to be contingent. This time-difference may seem a trivial matter at the present sketchy level of discussion, but it will gain in importance as our analysis gains in precision. It is in practice frequently obscured by the fact that the environmental circumstances which evoke a given response are often constant and hence are the same circumstances as those which the response meets upon its execution.

The notion of appropriate response is thus seen to link four primary and spatio-temporally distinct elements:

1. The environmental circumstances or events which act as stimuli and evoke the response.
2. The response.
3. The environmental circumstances which the response meets during its execution and on which its success depends.

4. The occurrence of a certain event or state of affairs, viz. the so-called 'goal' of the response, as an effect of the interaction between (2) and (3).

Let us continue the present analysis with the aid of a concrete example. Let this example be one whose essential features could be realized either by a living organism or by a machine, so that we have for the present a simple guarantee that we shall not stray from relationships known to be compatible with the general laws of physics, and that we shall continue to think of appropriateness and adaptation in the non-psychological sense in which they have become important in biology. And let the response to be taken as example be one which acts on the environment only at a single instant of time, so that the temporal relationships involved take on a particularly simple form.

These requirements are aptly met by the example of a rifleman aiming his rifle at a moving, e.g. flying, target. The action of aiming the rifle at the approaching target may be fully representative of an appropriate response. Nor is this type of response confined to rational agents, or indeed living beings. Many animals have the power of aiming, and, what is more, all the essential features of this example could be reproduced mechanically by a radar-controlled and automatically sighted anti-aircraft gun shooting at a flying target. If at any time the discussion of the rifleman leaves us in doubt whether we are using our concepts in a sense in which they could be applied to animals other than rational thinking agents, a simple switchover to such examples as a cat leaping at a mouse will settle the matter. And if we should be in doubt whether we are using our concepts in a sense compatible with the general concepts of macroscopically deterministic physics, a similar changeover to the example of the anti-aircraft gun will again answer our query. The example also fulfils the requirement that the response of the rifleman or gun only acts on the environment at a single instant of time, viz. at the moment of firing.

In terms of this example the notion of the appropriateness

of the gun's or rifle's line of fire involves again the same four spatio-temporally distinct elements:

1. The stimulus evoking the response may be assumed to be the appearance of the target within a given region, e.g. within the field of vision of the rifleman, or within the area swept by the radar beam. Let this stimulus be taken to occur at the time t_0, and be denoted by S_{t_0}. For simplicity let us also provisionally assume that the rifleman or gun-predictor appraises the target's course from a single look or a single set of measurements, and that this is taken at t_0.

2. The relevant part of the response itself consists of the line of fire adopted by the rifle or gun. Let t_1 be the time of firing, and let the direction in which the rifle or gun aims at that time, i.e. its line of fire, be denoted by R_{t_1}.

3. The environmental circumstances with which the actual firing coincides and in relation to which that line of fire is, or is not, appropriate, consists of all those environmental t_1-factors which determine the path of the target during the time-of-flight of the bullet. This set of factors contains, of course, the position, velocity, and direction of the target at the inception of this time of flight, i.e. at t_1, plus all forces and conditions as they exist at t_1 which will determine the target's path during that interval. Let this whole set of environmental circumstances be denoted by E_{t_1}.

4. Finally, we have the fourth element, the hypothetical future event or the 'goal' of the action, whose occurrence as the result of the response is taken as the criterion of the response's appropriateness. Here it is necessary to proceed with a little caution for there may exist two alternative conceptions:

(a) We may interpret 'appropriateness' in the sense that the rifle or gun is said to have been aimed 'appropriately' only if the bullet subsequently actually hits the target. Let the occurrence of such a direct hit at some point of time t_2 be denoted by G_{t_2}.

(b) Alternatively, we may adopt the attitude that the rifle or gun may be said to have been aimed 'appropriately' if it merely created at the time of firing the greatest probability feasible under the given circumstances of the bullet striking the target. This is a broader conception and probably the more common one.

In 4 (*b*) the path of the target and/or the bullet is conceived to be undetermined in some respects, and not, therefore, with certainty predictable by the rifleman or gun-predictor. In the present context this must not, of course, be taken to mean that the motion of the target or bullet is indeterministic in the sense that it is not accountable in terms of preceding physical events. Rather, it means that some of the factors which determine their paths are assumed to be unknown by the rifleman or that they cannot be taken into account by the gun-predictor. Typical factors of this kind are the wind velocity, random variations in the path of the target or, if the target is a living object, sudden unforeseeable impulses to change the direction of motion. Broadly speaking, the path of the target or bullet in that case can only be predicted subject to the hypothetical exclusion of the unknown factors. The predicted path is then not the actual path but merely an *ideal*, viz. the probable path—although the two may, of course, coincide. For instance, it is presumably true to say that both the ordinary rifleman and a simple gun-predictor work on the simplifying assumption that the target will pursue its course with constant speed and in a straight line during the time of flight of the bullet or shell. The exact meaning of 'probable path' in this context need not detain us at the present stage, provided we remember that in the sense of 4 (*b*) a statement about the appropriateness of the line of fire is not a direct statement about the actual situation but about an ideal situation which has all the main relationships in common with the actual situation except that abstraction is made of a certain number of interfering factors. As long as this distinction between 4 (*a*) and 4 (*b*) is kept in mind, there is no reason why we should not accord both cases the same analytical treatment. S_{t_0}, R_{t_1}, E_{t_1}, and G_{t_2} now refer to the corresponding events or conditions in either the actual *or* the ideal situation, it being understood that in the latter case they exclude all those unknown factors from which this ideal picture makes abstraction.

To elucidate the temporal and causal relationships which exist between the above four elements on the assumption of an appropriately aimed shot, we may enter these into a diagram in which the horizontal direction is used as a time coordinate, but in which no definite meaning is attached to the vertical direction beyond that of physical distinctness. If in this diagram we represent a causal connexion by an arrow, the relations between S_{t_0}, R_{t_1}, E_{t_1}, and G_{t_2} which have so far emerged may be symbolized as follows:

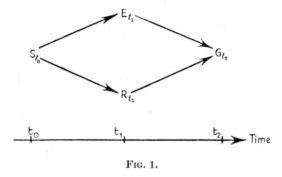

Fig. 1.

After these preliminaries let us now investigate the exact meaning of 'appropriateness' when the rifle's or gun's line of fire is stated to be appropriate in relation to the path of the target and from the point of view of scoring a direct hit. Does the term 'appropriate' in this context merely mean that the line of fire is *effective* in scoring a hit? The answer to this important question is No. Although the idea of 'appropriateness' implies that of 'efficacy' it also transcends the latter in at least one important respect: The idea of 'efficacy' covers only the *given* situation or its development, whereas, if we say that under given circumstances a certain line of fire is 'appropriate' we envisage not only the given course of the target but at the same time compare it before the mind's eye with an extended range of possible *alternative* courses which the target might have taken and for each of which there exists one, and usually only one, effective line of fire. Each one of these respective lines of fire is called the 'appropriate' one in relation to the corresponding path of the target. In other words, the statement that a given line of fire is 'appropriate' in relation to a given course of the target, asserts that the given course of the target is a member of a set of possible alternative courses and that the given line of fire is the corresponding member of a correlated set of possible alternative lines of fire, each member of the latter set being effective in conjunction with the corresponding member of the former.

The notion of appropriateness, therefore, is based on a vague consideration of a set $E'_{t_1}, E''_{t_1}, E'''_{t_1},...$, of alternative circumstances and a correlated set $R'_{t_1}, R''_{t_1}, R'''_{t_1},...$, of effective responses, the members of the two sets standing in a one-one correspondence such that under the given conditions only corresponding pairs of members will lead to a direct hit. These two sets are not sets of actual events but sets of imagined alternatives to actual events, the alternatives differing from one another by the hypothetical variation of some point of detail, e.g. variation in the target's direction. The whole idea is the result of a creative act of thought. From Gibbsian thermodynamics we may borrow the name *ensemble* for such a set of events, situations, or systems created in our thoughts as exact counterparts of one another except for one or more properties which are hypothetically varied according to a freely chosen principle. This principle of construction may be called the *generative principle* of the respective ensemble.

According to the above analysis an appropriate response is an effective response which is conceived against the background of an ensemble of alternative sets of environmental circumstances and as a member of a correlated ensemble of effective responses. In one point of detail this account requires a slight qualification in the present example and, probably, in most practical cases. The ensemble of alternative paths of the target is not usually conceived to be a finite ensemble: its membership has the power of a continuum, since we do not usually envisage a discrete number of alternative paths but a continuous (although finite) range of variation of the target's path. The aggregate of alternative paths is not thought of member by member but merely in terms of its approximate limits.

The exact meaning of the term 'possible' in the context of 'possible alternative paths of the target' will become clearer as we go along. The original context in which the concept of 'appropriateness' was formed was no doubt psychological and referred to rational beings which have a set of alternative responses ready to meet alternative circumstances, and which are conceived to be free to choose the appropriate response from this set of available responses. The 'possible' alternative circumstances are then merely the different circumstances which have frequently occurred in their experience, or have been recorded by others. But when this idea of appropriateness is applied to activities which do not spring from a conscious and rationally thinking mind, and when its meaning, therefore, becomes metaphorical in comparison with this psychological use, the term 'possible' also shifts its meaning and the whole matter becomes more intricate. However, these considerations concern merely the range of variation embraced by the given ensemble and do not alter the essential fact that when we think of appropriateness we envisage a finite range of hypothetical variations of the actual environmental circumstances in conjunction with a correlated ensemble of effective responses.

§ 8. *Transition to the Concept of Adaptation*

In making the transition to the concept of adaptation we must distinguish the activity of *adapting* any X to any Y from the relationship of *adaptedness* between X and Y which this activity establishes. That is to say, in our ballistic example we must distinguish the activity of taking aim from the relationship of adaptedness which it establishes between the line of fire and the course of the target. Let us take the concept of 'adaptedness' in this latter sense as the primary concept.

The first thing to note is that in the usual biological context the idea of 'adaptedness' implies *appropriateness*. We would not consider the falcon's flight to be adapted to the direction taken by its prey unless it were appropriate to minimising the distance between them. In fact, it is only in the special psychological sense and when referring to rational beings who are pursuing a consciously conceived goal that we might find an exception to this. For it is only in this psychological sense that we might call an activity adapted to the environment merely on the grounds that it happens to spring from a subjective desire on the part of the agent to act appropriately—irrespective of whether or not the action turns out to be successful and appropriate in the objective sense. But in spite of the fact that this psychological use may have been the original use of the words 'adapted' and 'adaptation', in biology these words have found common currency without any desire on the part of the speaker to attribute the presence of a rational and conscious mind to the organism concerned, and, as I have stressed in Chapter I, it is only this significant meaning of adaptation that we intend to analyse. In this sense, therefore, to say that the organic response X is adapted to the environmental circumstances Y from the point of view of some future state of affairs Z towards the realization of which it is conceived to be directed, implies that it is appropriate and hence also that it is effective in bringing about the actual or probable occurrence of Z.

The crucial question, however, which we must now take up is whether or not any significant relationships other than those of appropriateness and efficacy are implied by the concept of adaptation. Or must we assume adaptedness and appropriateness to be synonymous? The writings of most mechanists imply an affirmative answer to this last question. According to this view, to say that an organic action is adapted in certain respects, means no more than that it is appropriate in those respects. It cannot be presumed that the adherents of this restricted interpretation ever felt very happy about their attitude, but so long as they had found no way of scientifically formulating any other implication of the concept of adaptation their scientific discipline and honesty left no alternative open. In extreme cases 'adaptation' was even rendered synonymous with mere 'efficacy'. Witness this statement from a leading contemporary treatise on the general principles of life: 'Organisms are adapted to their environments. And all that this means is that their characteristics are such that in these environments they are able to live.' But can it really be true that 'adaptation' means no more than these utterly trivial relationships of mere efficacy? Can it be true that generations of biologists have meant no more than this when they found in that concept a vehicle for expressing the most distinctive features of living systems and organic activities? Are not these simple causal relations such as can be found in any inorganic system? Can we really maintain that the cloud is adapted to the sun in the same sense as that in which, for instance, the path of the pursuing hound can be said to be adapted to that of the fleeing hare?

The idea that adaptedness implies no more than appropriateness is equally quickly dispelled by concrete examples. For instance, if this doctrine were true, any fish could significantly be said to be adapted to any aquarium in which it survives, in spite of the fact that we would usually regard the aquarium as the adapted object. And there is another weighty reason which speaks against the idea that adaptedness is synonymous with either appropriateness or efficacy. For it is possible to name an important category of organic activities which are called 'appropriate' and 'effective' but which would certainly not be called 'adapted'. I mean all those actions which we are wont to describe as 'accidentally appropriate': the rifle or gun goes off accidentally during loading and by a rare stroke of fortune the target is hit. The line of fire will in such a case be called 'accidentally efficacious' or 'accidentally appropriate', but certainly not 'adapted'. Again, a gene-mutation may have accidentally appropriate effects in respect of the survival of the species, but the variant characteristic does not become a case of 'adaptation' in the full sense until its selective advantages have caused it to become firmly established in the population and have therefore made its existence in the population more than an accident. The meaning of 'accidental' in these contexts will be discussed at a later stage. Suffice it to say here that we have no reason to consider the term 'accidental' to be meaningless in the present context and that we may take it to specify a definite category of organic responses which are appropriate under the given environmental circumstances without being adapted to these circumstances.

No more need be said to reveal the far-going inadequacy of any interpretation of adaptation which equates it merely with either appropriateness or efficacy. We must, therefore, regard it as our next task to discover what the idea of adaptation implies in addition to these two concepts.

The example of the automatic gun will come to our aid in this respect. In terms of this example our question is: if we say that, at the time t_1 of firing, the gun's line of fire R_{t_1} was adapted to the movement of the target E_{t_1} from the point of view of securing a direct hit G_{t_2}, is it true to say that we mean no more than that at that instant the gun's line of fire was such as to cause the target to be hit?

The answer to this question is in the negative and we can now see why. For, surely, we mean in addition that, at the time of making this appropriate response to the movement of the target, the gun-training mechanism was objectively so conditioned that there existed a definite range of possible variations of the target's path such that, whatever other course the target *might* have taken (within certain limits: see below), the mechanism *would* have responded by an appropriate modification of the gun's line of fire. We mean not only, therefore, that the gun's line of fire was appropriate in the given instance and in relation to one single given path of the target, but in addition that this appropriateness was secured by objective system-properties of the gun-training mechanism which would also have caused any one of an extended range of *alternative* paths to have been matched by an appropriate line of fire.

It is in this special sense that the objective system properties which the automatic gun possesses when in working order
come to raise the occurrences of direct hits on the target above
the level of pure chance coincidence. And it is in the same sense
that adaptive behaviour, or an adaptive evolutionary change,
in the animal world comes to assume that typical character
of involving an objectively biased and non-accidental occurrence of appropriateness and success.

Two sets of elements are said to be 'correlated' if we can
establish a one-one correspondence between their members
such that to each member of the one set there corresponds one
and only one member of the other set. In terms of this notion
of correlated sets of elements the relation between the ideas of
efficacy, appropriateness, and adaptation which has so far
emerged may be summed up as follows:

1. The response R_{t_1} is *effective* in relation to the environmental circumstances E_{t_1} and in respect of the subsequent
occurrence of the 'goal' G_{t_2}, if the joint occurrence of R_{t_1} and
E_{t_1} causes the subsequent occurrence of G_{t_2}.

2. R_{t_1} is *appropriate* in relation to the circumstances E_{t_1} and
in respect of the subsequent occurrence of G_{t_2}, if E_{t_1} is a member of a hypothetical set or ensemble $E'_{t_1}, E''_{t_1}, E'''_{t_1},...$ of possible alternative environmental circumstances while R_{t_1} is the
corresponding member of a correlated set $R'_{t_1}, R''_{t_1}, R'''_{t_1},...$ of
possible alternative responses, each member of the latter set
being effective in bringing about G_{t_2} if and only if it occurs in
conjunction with the corresponding member of the former
set.

3. Finally, the statement that R_{t_1} is *adapted* to E_{t_1} in respect
of G_{t_2} means that the organism or mechanism causally determining R_{t_1} is objectively so conditioned that if certain changed
initial circumstances had caused the occurrence of any alterna-
tive member of the set $E'_{t_1}, E''_{t_1}, E'''_{t_1},...$ it would in each case also
have caused the occurrence of the corresponding member of
the correlated set $R'_{t_1}, R''_{t_1}, R'''_{t_1},...$ of appropriate responses.

It will be seen from these results that the assertion that a
given response is 'appropriate' under given environmental

circumstances tells us no more about the actual situation than the statement that it is effective—although it tells us something of the degrees of freedom which the given situation is imagined to have, i.e. something about our conception of that situation. In contrast, the statement that a given response is 'adapted' to given environmental circumstances does tell us more about the given situation than the mere assertion of efficacy. Because it tells us that the rifleman, the gun, the organism, or whatever the case may be, *is* such that under this or that alternative set of circumstances it *would* have reacted in this or that modified way. We noted above that adaptation was a form of non-accidental appropriateness: in the objective system property formulated in the last sentence we have the objective basis of this non-accidentality.

In relation to our concrete ballistic example the meaning of 'adaptation' may be expressed as follows: the gun's actual line of fire (R_{t_1}) is *adapted* to the target's path and the factors that influence it (E_{t_1}), if (a) the gun-plus-target system is at that time so ordered that a direct hit will be scored, and (b) there exists a hypothetical range of variation of E_{t_1} such that if certain changed initial circumstances had caused E_{t_1} to adopt other values within this range, then R_{t_1} would have adopted just those new and different values which in each such case would have led to the scoring of a direct hit. In short: the gun's line of fire *was* appropriate *and would have been* appropriate had the initial circumstances been otherwise.

The nature of the 'changed initial circumstances' referred to in these definitions will be discussed in the following section.

§ 9. *The Coenetic Variable*

The only causal connexions explicitly referred to in the preceding discussion and definition of 'adaptation' are the two shown in Fig. 2.

Only three of the four elements involved in the concept of appropriateness (pp. 38–46) and illustrated in Fig. 1, p. 44, have so far entered our definition of adaptation and in this

respect, therefore, the latter is still incomplete. To complete
the definition we shall find that we must add an explicit
reference to a fourth event or state of affairs. This fourth
element may or may not be identical with the stimulus S_{t_0} but
it is similarly connected with E_{t_1} and R_{t_1}, and it is a necessary
ingredient of any instance of adaptation in the sense of the
preceding definition (§ 8).

The need for an explicit reference to such a fourth element
becomes at once evident when it is asked how the one-one

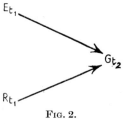

FIG. 2.

correspondence, to which our definition
refers, between alternative values of
E_{t_1} and the correspondingly modified
values of R_{t_1}, can in practice be brought
about, having in mind that these two
sets of factors belong to the same instant
of time and are therefore incapable of
causally determining each other. The
only way in which this correlation is physically possible is
through *joint causation*, i.e. when there exists some prior
environmental state of affairs or event which enters into
the causal determination of both E_{t_1} and R_{t_1}, and of which
both, therefore, are parallel effects. We shall call this necessary common causal determinant of E_{t_1} and R_{t_1} the *coenetic
variable* of the adaptation. Our definition of adaptation must
therefore be enlarged by the requirement that the hypothetical
variations of E_{t_1} to which this definition refers, comprises only
such variations as result from the hypothetical variations of
a coenetic variable, i.e. of a factor which is also a causal determinant of R_{t_1}. In other words, the 'changed initial circumstances' referred to in that definition must be interpreted to
mean variations of the t_0-values of one or more coenetic variables of the adaptation. In our ballistic example the coenetic
variables of the adaptation between R_{t_1} and E_{t_1} consist of all
those prior factors entering into the determination of the
target's subsequent flight that the rifleman or the gun-predictor 'take account of' in determining their line of fire. Usually
these factors will consist of the values which the position,

direction and velocity of the target have at a point of time, say t_0, which precedes t_1 by the reaction lag of the rifleman or the gun-training mechanism.

If we denote any one of these coenetic variables by CV and its value at t_0 by CV_{t_0}, we may represent the four principal elements involved in the adaptedness of the gun's or rifle's line of fire to the target's path, and the causal connexions between them, by the following diagram.

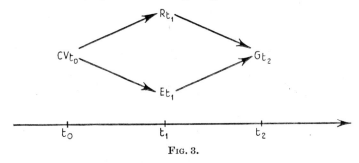

FIG. 3.

The necessity for the existence of one or more coenetic variables in every case of adaptation is also intuitively obvious. It is impossible for any machine or living organism to adapt a certain action to the environment unless it has information about the environment, i.e. unless it can be influenced by some features of that environment. These features are in the last analysis always features existing prior to the adapted action concerned. Adaptation by means of rational prediction is no exception to this rule. For every prediction argues to future events from the state of affairs existing prior to the actual act of predicting. If the gun-training mechanism or the rifleman in determining a line of fire were prevented from taking any factors connected with the target's prior path into account, they would be acting merely 'blindly'. They could in that case bring about an accidentally appropriate line of fire but never an adapted one. The metaphorical comparison with blindness is illuminating in this connexion, because it under-lines the fact that a fundamental biological function of the eyes, and for that matter of all sense organs, is precisely to establish causal connexions which will enable environmental variables to become the coenetic variables of adapted organic behaviour.

If adaptive actions are of the nature of responses, in other words, if they are evoked by specific environmental stimuli, the stimulating events may at the same time be the coenetic variables of the adaptation. But this is not necessarily so. While one set of environmental circumstances may evoke or release a given action, another set may provide the main influence in shaping the details of its execution.

§ 10. *Directive Correlation*

In the preceding section the essential incompleteness of our provisional explication of adaptation was seen to be this: As generative principle of the ensemble $E'_{t_1}, E''_{t_1}, E'''_{t_1}, \ldots$ only those variations of E_{t_1} are to be allowed which are entailed by the independent variation of a coenetic variable, i.e. of an event or state of affairs which is prior to, and a *joint* causal determinant of, both E_{t_1} and R_{t_1}.

On the strength of these considerations we shall now formulate the following provisional definition to introduce a new concept which will play a leading part in the remainder of the book, viz. the concept of *directive correlation*. It will become our main instrument for expressing in precise terms the various forms of purposiveness found in nature.

Definition. Any event or state of affairs R_{t_1} occurring at a time t_1 is *directively correlated* to a given simultaneous event or state of affairs E_{t_1} in respect of the subsequent occurrence of an event or state of affairs G_{t_2} if the physical system of which these are part is objectively so conditioned that there exists an event or state of affairs CV_{t_0} prior to t_1, and a set of possible alternative values of CV_{t_0}, such that

(a) under the given circumstances any variation of CV_{t_0} within this set implies variations of both R_{t_1} and E_{t_1};

(b) any such pair of varied values of R_{t_1}, E_{t_1} (as well as the pair of their actual values) is a pair of corresponding members of two correlated sets of possible values

$R'_{t_1}, R''_{t_1}, R'''_{t_1}, \ldots$ and $E'_{t_1}, E''_{t_1}, E'''_{t_1}, \ldots$, which are such that under the circumstances all pairs of corresponding members, but no other pairs, cause the subsequent occurrence of G_{t_2}.

Our previous analysis of adaptation shows that every adaptation is an instance of directive correlation, but not vice versa. Directive correlation is a slightly wider concept. For inspection of the usual meaning of 'adaptation' shows that in the case of an organism-plus-environment system the coenetic variable consists always of an environmental variable and, in fact, usually of an antecedent value of the environmental variable to which a given response is regarded as adapted (cf. § 13). On the other hand, directive correlation, as defined above, contains none of these restrictions concerning the coenetic variable. Incidentally, the latter of these two restrictions sometimes leads us to speak of adaptation as existing not between R_{t_1} and E_{t_1}, but between R_{t_1} and CV_{t_0}. This is, for instance, the case in such phrases as 'the animal *is* adapting itself to the chang*ed* circumstances'. This variant of the normal use of the term, however, in no way affects the intrinsic relationships implied by the concept of adaptation.

It will be noted that in the definition of directive correlation, and also in our interpretation of adaptation, we are now no longer confined to those activities which are classed as 'responses'. All forms of physical activity come within the orbit of our definitions and we can henceforth ignore the special case of so-called 'responses'. As far as the causal determination of adaptive activity is concerned we have seen that it is the existence of coenetic variables which counts and not the existence of specific stimuli. In other words, the emphasis has shifted from environmental factors which evoke a given organic action to the general class of factors which determine its specific nature.

In the second place, it should be noted that our definition of directive correlation applies to living organisms in exactly the same sense as to dead machines of the type of our anti-aircraft gun. For, although we were mainly guided by the latter example, it is evidently possible in exactly the same sense to assert of the rifleman that, *qua* living organism, he was at the time of taking aim objectively so conditioned that this or that varied path of the target would have evoked this or that modification of his line of fire. Of course, it may be more difficult to verify such assertions about the rifleman than about the anti-aircraft gun, but this is a different question which will be discussed later on and which does not impair the significance of the assertions as such.

In fact, it can be said that there are no adaptive vital activities (in that biologically so significant sense of 'apparently goal-directed activities') in which we cannot reveal exact counterparts to the variables and causal connexions in terms of which we defined 'directive correlation'. Directive correlation, in short, is the fundamental and objective system-property which in more or less complex forms underlies the phenomena of adaptation in nature and their purpose-like character. We have therefore succeeded in formulating this purpose-like character in terms which, although not yet quite up to the level of physico-mathematical precision (this will have to wait until Chapter III), yet are sufficiently precise and definite to go on with.

An important point to note is that although we have defined the directive correlation between E_{t_1} and R_{t_1} in terms of a future event, viz. the occurrence of a direct hit on the target (G_{t_2}), there was nothing in the least teleological in this definition. Our definition of directive correlation does not in the least imply that this future event G_{t_2} is a cause of either E_{t_1} or R_{t_1}, or that in any sense whatsoever it enters into their causal determination. The definition of directive correlation employs a reference to G_{t_2} only as a criterion in specifying the one-one correspondence which the gun-training mechanism effects (when in working order) between a certain range of alternative paths of the target and the gun's lines of fire—i.e. in specifying the correlation between the sets $E'_{t_1}, E''_{t_1}, E'''_{t_1}, ...,$ and $R'_{t_1}, R''_{t_1}, R'''_{t_1}, ...$ There is nothing teleological, in the sense of the future determining the present through some form of 'final

causation', in the behaviour of the automatic gun. Its mode
of operation is strictly mechanical and deterministic. The fact
that the engineers who designed the gun may have been thinking about future targets and future direct hits has nothing to
do with this particular issue. It merely means that certain
states of consciousness of the engineers concerned entered into
the determination of the design and construction of the gun;
and that does not in the least alter the fact that in the gun-
plus-target system we have a physical system which may be
regarded as closed and in which nothing but straightforward
physical causation is at work during the events which we
refer to when we assert that the gun's line of fire is adapted
to (or directively correlated with) the path of the target.

At the present, and still comparatively vague, level of discussion it already emerges, therefore, that 'adaptation' in its
biological and purpose-like meaning can be paraphrased in perfectly orthodox causal-analytical terms. In fact, when we
reach the physico-mathematical definition of directive correlation given in § 20 we shall see that it specifies an objective
system property of material systems which may be regarded
as just as respectable a physical property as any dealt with
in orthodox physics.

The reader may at first see a difficulty in the fact that we
have defined 'directive correlation' and 'adaptation' in terms
of purely hypothetical conditions. For, in defining the property
which the gun-training mechanism possesses when in working
order, we referred not only to the gun's actual behaviour in a
single concrete instance, but in addition to the gun's behaviour
under hypothetically varied circumstances: *if* the target had
taken a different course the gun-training mechanism *would* have
caused the gun's line of fire to be modified accordingly. The
elements of our ensembles are, all but one, imaginary elements.

But this difficulty is only apparent, because from the
scientific point of view there is nothing epistemologically
difficult in this reference to hypothetical conditions. The concept of directive correlation and adaptation in this respect
implies merely that the gun-controlling mechanism *is* such

that under such-and-such circumstances such-and-such things *would* have happened. And to specify actual properties of given material systems in terms of the systems' reactions under hypothetically varied circumstances is scientifically not only legitimate (provided, of course, that the hypothetically assumed conditions do not involve us in contradictions), but is in fact one of the fundamental modes of physical description. The physical principle of virtual variation and classical thermo-dynamics, for instance, make explicit use of this method, and we may even go so far as to say that this idea is implied in most simple physical statements. For instance, to say that the object X has a temperature Y means to the physicist little else than that such-and-such a process of measuring *when* applied to the object X *would* lead to the pointer-reading Y. And just as it can be significantly asserted that X has the tem-perature Y at a time when no measurements are actually being made, so it can be significantly asserted that the gun-training mechanism has the objective system-property of directive correlation irrespective of whether this property is at the time put to the test by confronting the gun with a succession of targets pursuing alternative paths. The notion of causality, too, will be seen in § 18 to depend on a similar comparison between actual and hypothetically varied situa-tions. Moreover, a similar state of affairs prevails in every-day life: if we say that the table *is* hard, we mean, strictly speaking, that it *is* such that it *would* resist if pressure were applied.

It was seen above that the concept of adaptation refers not merely to a dyadic relationship—as the syntactical structure of the statement 'R_{t_1} is adapted to E_{t_1}' might lead one to suppose —but essentially to a disguised tetradic relationship. Four elements are involved in the tetrad, viz. the elements exempli-fied above by CV_{t_0}, E_{t_1}, R_{t_1}, G_{t_2}, and four causal connexions between them (Fig. 3). Moreover, it was seen that the concept of adaptation does not actually predicate anything of these four relationships, but, rather, by means of implications con-cerning their effects under hypothetically varied circumstances specifies an objective system property of the material system involved—in our examples, of the rifleman or of the gun. Upon careful analysis, therefore, the predicate 'adapted' turns out to be an extremely oblique predicate: To call an action 'adapted' is really making a statement about the agent rather than about the action. The properties the statement attributes to him are such that they can only be formulated explicitly by referring to hypothetically varied circumstances. No wonder adaptation and related concepts have for so long confounded the biologists, philosophers, and theologians. There is something almost pathetic in the obstinate search of some philosophers for specific properties of purpose-like activities in nooks and atomic interstices in which the predicate of adaptation never asserted them to exist in the first place. No wonder they returned empty handed and felt driven to the conclusion that from the scientific point of view the purposiveness of organic activities is a meaningless concept.

§ 11. *The Focal Condition*

In our analysis of the directive correlation between the gun's line of fire and the target's path, the occurrence of a direct hit was seen to be the criterion in terms of which the respective correlation was defined. In the sequel we shall call the event or state of affairs which functions as the corresponding criterion in any case of directive correlation the *focal condition* of that directive correlation. We introduce this term, therefore, generally to replace the rather misleading words 'goal', 'end', or 'aims' in connexion with adaptive and purpose-like behaviour in biological systems.

The elementary pattern of the causal connexions involved whenever two physical events or conditions are directively correlated, was illustrated in Fig. 3. I have called this the *elementary* pattern of directive correlation because actual situations may, of course, be far more complicated than this simple diagram suggests. In many instances of directive correlation or adaptation there will be more than one coenetic variable, more than one focal condition, and more than two directively correlated variables. Thus, a directive correlation between five correlated variables with one coenetic variable and one focal condition would involve a pattern of causal connexions of the following type:[1]

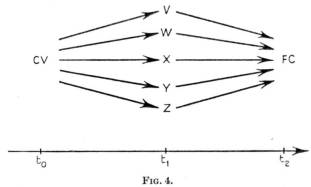

The peculiar property of any focal condition is that the directive correlation with which it is associated imparts to it a special kind of independence from the effects of events which have entered into its history. For, although the event or state of affairs FC is causally connected with the values which the correlated variables V, W, X, Y, Z, assume at t_1, and although these in turn are causally connected with the value of the coenetic variable CV at t_0, the occurrence of FC at t_2 is itself independent of the latter (at least within a certain range of variation). In terms of our ballistic example: although the occurrence of a direct hit at t_2 is causally dependent on both R_{t_1} and E_{t_1}, and although both E_{t_1} and R_{t_1} are in turn causally dependent on the target's position, direction, velocity, &c. at t_0, viz. on CV_{t_0}, yet the adaptation of the gun's line of fire ensures that, within certain finite limits, hypothetical variations of CV_{t_0} will not affect the subsequent occurrence of a direct hit. We shall return to the investigation of this special independence between CV_{t_0} and G_{t_2} presently.

---

[1] The similarity between such schemata and the convergence of light rays in passing through a convex lens accounts for my original choice of the term 'focal condition'.

§ 12. *Degrees of Adaptation*

It was seen in § 9 that any instance of directive correlation between two or more variables requires the existence of at least one coenetic variable. It was also seen that the coenetic variable is the basic independent variable in the concept of adaptation and that its variation constitutes the generating principle of the ensemble which this concept envisages.

The range of variation of the coenetic variable over which a given instance of directive correlation remains valid is usually limited. The automatic gun or the rifleman can adapt their line of fire only to a limited range of variation of the target's course, and they can take into account only a limited number of factors which determine this course. This suggests that if it is possible to attach some measure to the magnitude of the range within which a coenetic variable can be varied without the directive correlation breaking down, then this may be taken as a measure of the *degree* of directive correlation. Two further quantities which may be taken to indicate degrees of directive correlation are: the number of coenetic variables and the number of directively correlated variables. There are therefore several senses in which it is possible to distinguish between different degrees of directive correlation in similar systems. In the same senses it is accordingly possible to give precise meanings to the ideas of 'degree of adaptation' and 'degrees of purposiveness' in the comparison of similar physical systems.

§ 13. *The Asymmetry of Adaptation*

The relationship of adaptation, in the dyadic form in which it appears syntactically as in the sentence 'X is adapted to Y', is asymmetrical: 'X is adapted to Y' does not imply 'Y is adapted to X'. Directive correlation, on the other hand, is a symmetrical relationship as far as the correlated variables are concerned. The concept of adaptation, therefore, cannot be regarded as strictly synonymous with 'directive correlation' and represents only a special case. In § 10 this qualification was already indicated but the point requires a few additional remarks.

Consider again our ballistic example. In that example the coenetic variable consisted of the set of t_0-values of a number of physical variables connected with the motion of the target, e.g. its direction, velocity, &c., at the time t_0. They were the variables which the gun-predictor or the rifleman takes into account in predicting the target's course. Meanwhile, E_{t_1} comprised the respective t_1 values of the target's direction, velocity, &c. In other words, in this particular case the coenetic variable could really have been represented by the symbol E_{t_0}. And if we look for other examples of adaptation we find this to be quite generally true: when we assert the value X_{t_1} of some variable X to be adapted to the value Y_{t_1} of a variable Y, we are referring to a directive correlation in which some prior value of Y, say Y_{t_0}, acts as the coenetic variable, i.e. in which $CV_{t_0} \equiv Y_{t_0}$.

Take, for instance, a case already alluded to in § 8, and consider the difference between asserting that the size of a certain fish is adapted to the size of its aquarium, and asserting that the size of the aquarium is adapted to the size of the fish. In the former case we imply that if the size of the aquarium had been different this would have entailed a different choice of fish; in the latter case the implication is that if the size of the fish had been different this would have led to a different choice of aquarium. In the first assertion, therefore, we are dealing with a case of adaptation in which the size of the aquarium at some prior point of time is regarded as coenetic variable, whereas, in the second assertion the size of the fish, as it was at the time when the aquarium was chosen, acts as the coenetic variable.

If all this be accepted as the correct interpretation of the most common and significant biological meaning of 'adaptation', we may summarize our preliminary analysis of this concept by giving it the following explication:

The statement that an event or state of affairs X_{t_1} is *adapted* to another event or state of affairs Y_{t_1} from the point of view of some future event or condition FC_{t_2}, means that X_{t_1} and Y_{t_1} are connected by a directive correlation which has FC_{t_2} as focal condition and in which a prior value of Y, say Y_{t_0}, acts as coenetic variable.

The asymmetry of adaptation discussed in this section suggests at least one reason why, for instance, in the conception of the gun's line of fire being adapted to the target's motion, the 'responsibility' for this adaptation is always attributed to the gun-training mechanism, in spite of the fact that this mechanism is only responsible for *one* of the two chains of causal connexion which link the coenetic variable with the focal condition. The reason is that E_{t_1} is a causal function of E_{t_0} more or less as a matter of course, whereas the special interference of the gun-training mechanism is required to make R_{t_1} a causal function of E_{t_0}, and particularly to make it the kind of function of E_{t_0} which will result in a directive correlation.

The reader who has been made a little apprehensive about the exact meaning of 'causal connexion' or 'causal function' in the present context, and about the legitimacy of, for instance, regarding the past size of the aquarium as one of the causal determinants of its present size, or regarding E_{t_0} as a causal determinant of E_{t_1}, is referred to § 18 where the concepts of causal connexion and causal function will be given a precise physico-mathematical definition.

§ 14. *The Independence of the Focal Condition and the Coenetic Variable*

We have seen that if a physical event or state of affairs X_{t_1} is directively correlated to another event or state of affairs Y_{t_1}, with a certain event or state of affairs FC_{t_2} as focal condition and with CV_{t_0} as coenetic variable, the correlation between X_{t_1} and Y_{t_1} renders the occurrence of the condition FC_{t_2} independent of variations of CV_{t_0} (provided these remain within certain limits) in spite of the fact that FC_{t_2} is causally connected with X_{t_1} and Y_{t_1} and that each of these in turn is causally connected with CV_{t_0}. For instance, the effect of the adaptive action of the gun-training mechanism in our ballistic example was to render the occurrence of G_{t_2} independent, within a certain range of variation, of E_{t_0}, in spite of the fact that the occurrence of G_{t_2} is causally connected with both E_{t_1} and R_{t_1}, and that these in turn are causally connected with E_{t_0}.

The nature of this special type of independence merits closer attention: it is an independence which is not based on the absence of causal chains between FC_{t_2} and CV_{t_0}, but on the fact that there are at least two such chains (the one involving X_{t_1} and the other involving Y_{t_1}) and that the partial effects of these two chains exactly compensate or offset each other.

We have here another example of the importance of giving the concept of causal connexion a precise definition: Can FC_{t_2} in this case be said to be causally connected with CV_{t_0} at all? Those who stress the transitiveness of causal connectivity will be inclined to answer this question affirmatively. An equally good case can, however, be made out for the opposite answer, since it may be argued that FC_{t_2} cannot be said to be causally connected with CV_{t_0} if variations of the latter have no effect on the former. For the clarification of these issues the reader is again referred to § 18.

One of the fundamental characteristics of living organisms is their independence from environmental fluctuations, and it has often been remarked that 'progress' in the living world consists largely of a growth of this independence. We are now in a position to see a little more clearly the general structure of the relationships which are responsible for the most important part of this independence, viz. for the independence enjoyed by the organism by virtue of adaptive or other purpose-like activities which have its survival as a focal condition. For inasmuch as this independence is due to the purpose-like character of the responses and internal adjustments which the organism makes to environmental disturbances, it is precisely the type of independence which we have just discussed, viz. the independence which the focal condition of a directive correlation enjoys in respect of variations of the coenetic variable.

We may assume that it were some such relationships of which, for instance, Rignano[1] was vaguely aware when he wrote of the strikingly purpose-like character of some organic activities: 'If we consider embryological phenomena or phenomena of regeneration we realise that when external circumstances change for an organism, the reaction processes produced by the change of circumstances also change, but that the final result of these processes, however different they may be as compared with one another, always remain the same'— and when he proposed this as a criterion for 'Finalism' in nature.

The main error of this passage and of similar passages with other authors is that they commit the 'genetic' fallacy of treating as a temporal sequence of compared situations what should properly be presented as a logical sequence of alternatives: they confuse actual successive temporal variants of a given situation with the hypothetical variations embodied in an ensemble. 'Directive correlation' as we have defined it does not refer to any correlation between pairs of elements belonging to any actual and temporal sequence of comparable situations. It specifies a property of one single given situation in terms of a purely imaginary ensemble of alternative situations. We may, of course, by way of experiment, actually attempt to realize these hypothetical variations: we may let the automatic gun of our example run through a temporal series of situations in which many of the hypothetical alternatives of the target's path are in turn actually realized. Such a test series of experiments would be the proper procedure to adopt if we wanted to verify whether the gun's line of fire really had the adaptive character which we claimed it had. But, as was remarked before, the significance of the assertion that the gun's line of fire has this adaptive character does not as such depend on the existence of such a test series of experiments. Directive correlation can be significantly asserted of single and non-recurring situations.

This question of verifiability is important because it is

---

[1] *Mind*, 1931.

notoriously difficult to conduct a test series of controlled experiments with living organisms. The type of test series usually required, and also required for the strict verification of any claim about directive correlation, consists of a series of repeated experiments which differ from one another only in the variation of the initial value of a single variable and in all other respects are performed under identical conditions. It is the most important type of experimental test series in physics and its practical impossibility in much biological material is a severe handicap for the biologist. But the only methodological significance of those practical difficulties is that they make the discovery and verification of functional relationships between biological variables more difficult. It does not in any sense affect the significance, as such, of biological hypotheses which assert the existence of certain functional relationships. If it did, not only biological theory but also physical theory would be impossible since the mathematical functions postulated in physics usually relate to an infinite set of values of the physical variables concerned, whereas, of course, no test series can comprise more than a finite number of measurements. No test series, therefore, can verify completely the existence of any functional relationship of this kind between physical or biological variables: it can only supply a number of tests which either encourage the scientist to accept a certain functional relationship between empirical variables as a hypothesis, or urge him to seek alternative hypotheses.

§ 15. *Directive Correlation and the Teleological Fallacy*

Our analysis and examples have shown that directive correlation is a physical property which can exist in a closed physical system without presupposing the presence within that system of a rational agent and of conscious mental processes, i.e. of processes which are purposive in the literal sense of the word and involve rational thought, the presence of visualized aims, and fixed resolutions in the mind of a thinking agent. It is therefore seen that conscious mental processes constitute but one of several possible mechanisms in nature which can cause a system to have the objective property of directive correlation. Moreover, our survey of the factual background in § 4 establishes without doubt that conscious mental processes in the above sense are the exception rather than the rule as causes of directive correlation.

Yet, however exceptional in living nature as a whole those directive correlations may be which arise from the conscious activity of rational agents, it is the only case of whose working Man has a direct and introspective knowledge. Hence, it came about that, as Man awoke to the objective phenomena of directive correlation in nature, he began to describe them in terms of concepts introspectively derived from his own experience, and to interpret them in terms of anthropomorphic and psychological analogies—in terms of 'purposes', 'goals', 'aims', &c. The resulting confusions in biology were fatal. Yet, when all is said, it cannot really be surprising that Man, being part of nature, found analogies in nature to his own behaviour which invited such extrapolation.

No doubt the concept of adaptation has such a psychological and anthropomorphic origin. Its original and, in a certain sense, literal meaning refers not to the objective system property which we have called 'directive correlation', but to quite a different, subjective, correlation: viz. to the subjective correlation which exists between Man's intended actions and the opportunities for realizing his ends which he rightly or wrongly believes to exist in his environment. This is a correlation which expresses no more than the fact that, given his goal and given his interpretation and assessment of the existing environmental circumstances, the nature of his *intended* actions is usually determined. The correlation, therefore, refers to a subjective psychological process and bears no necessary relation to the objective system properties of directive correlation (cf. § 29).

Gradually, however, Man's intensified study of nature brought about a subtle process of semantic transformation and the concept of adaptation began in its own right to denote the objective relations which our analysis has rendered explicit and which we have incorporated in the concept of 'directive correlation'. Thus in everyday and technical use 'adaptation' has changed from a subjective psychological term to the objective biological term which is occupying us at the moment. This new meaning of 'adaptation' has since continued to exist side by side with the old, and the schism between vitalism and mechanism resulted largely from the inability of biologists to keep these two meanings apart. This separation was of course no simple matter so long as these two distinct meanings had not been given explicit definitions. For instance, when we speak about 'right' or 'wrong', 'successful' or 'unsuccessful' adaptation we are using the concept in its psychological sense, since these predicates are based on a comparison between the goal desired by a rational agent and the results actually achieved by his purposive actions. They cannot, therefore, be applied to the concept of directive correlation. 'Successful (or unsuccessful) directive correlation' is a meaningless phrase.

Since this generalization of 'adaptation' in biology was a gradual and unconscious historical metamorphosis, it carried into the new ways of thinking all the terminological chattels of the original psychological meaning of 'adaptation', e.g. such terms as 'aim', 'purpose', 'striving', &c. This was unavoidable so long as the new conception had been given no adequate analysis and no new terminology had been made available to denote those elements and relations which were analogous to certain elements and relations in the old conception. It is for this reason that so many writers in biology still protest that they cannot adequately describe the really characteristic aspects of living nature without the use of such concepts as 'goal-directed activity', 'purposive striving', &c. But, as we now know, it is not really the concept of 'goal' or 'purpose' that they want. It is the concept of a future event whose occurrence is a defining property of the characteristic objective correlation which is found between organic activities and the environments they work in. In other words, what they want is the concept of the 'focal condition' in conjunction with that of 'directive correlation'.

In the chapter on 'Teleology and Causation' of his *Biological Principles* Woodger formulates the issue between these two apparently antithetical notions in the following terms, and I am quoting this passage at length because it is a clear statement of prevalent confusions in biology.

Any change in an organism following an environmental change either subserves the persistence of the organism or it does not. If the former is the case we can call it an 'appropriate response'. Now with our present ways of thinking there appear to be two ways of regarding such an occurrence. We can either ask: Did this happen 'appropriately' *in order* that the persistence of the organism should endure? Or we can ask: Did this just happen in this way and it 'happened' to be appropriate? The difference is expressed in the ordinary use of the terms 'deliberate' and 'accidental'. If we say that the 'appropriate' response occurred *in order* that the organism might persist we are giving the teleological answer in the strict sense of the term. This is what vitalism does. But if we say that the change just happened and was accidentally appropriate, this is equivalent to saying that no answer *can* be given. And it may be that this is all it will ever be possible to say.

The analysis of our ballistic example brings out the major error of this passage. It is a clear case of the fallacy of false disjunction. Being deliberately appropriate and being accidentally appropriate do not, as Woodger and many other modern biologists suppose, exhaust the field of possibilities. Our automatic gun evidently falls outside either of these two categories while it is in working order. And so does any other phenomenon of directive correlation, for such phenomena, as we have shown, represent an objectively biased happening of appropriateness. Woodger's account is equivalent to saying that a given number on a die turns up either accidentally or deliberately, the third important possibility, viz. that of weighted dice, being left out of account. It is precisely this third possibility which corresponds to the case of directive correlation and underlies the apparent purposiveness of vital activities. Contrary to the sense of Woodger's concluding remark we see therefore that a definite answer *can* be given and that it is neither the teleological answer of the vitalists nor the sceptical answer of the mechanists. In the preceding discussions we have given this answer in still comparatively vague terms and it now remains to develop it on a higher level of precision. Meanwhile, the fate which the pseudo-conflict between 'teleology' and 'causation' suffers at our hands, will have become clear: the ideas of 'final causes' and 'teleological causation' prove to be superfluous and are dismissed as scientifically sterile, but the objective purpose-like properties in nature for the interpretation of which these teleological concepts were invented, have emerged from the surrounding darkness as relations capable of exact formulation in orthodox scientific terms and, incidentally, as relations which, far from contradicting the idea of efficient causation, actually presuppose it.

MATHEMATICAL DEFINITION AND CLARIFICATION OF DIRECTIVE CORRELATION

§ 16. *Introductory Remarks*

THE result of our preliminary analysis of adaptation was to reduce the purpose-like character of life processes to an objective and physical system property which we called 'directive correlation'. This property was provisionally defined in § 10. We also convinced ourselves that it was compatible with a deterministic conception of physical processes and that its existence did not necessarily presuppose the intervention of rational mental activities. The purpose of the present chapter is to refine this concept further by reducing it to physico-mathematical terms, thus exposing in detail the exact spatio-temporal and functional relationships involved in the purpose-like character of life processes and biological organization.

Four related reasons call for this further refinement of our concepts and for their translation into the actual language of physics.

In the first place, as was argued in § 5, only the physico-mathematical language offers the highest attainable level of both formal and semantic exactitude and definiteness. The relationships with which we are concerned in the analysis of the purpose-like character of vital activities are so intricate that only on this level of precision can our theoretical problems be solved. The need for such precision became evident, for instance, when we inquired into the exact meaning of 'causal connexion'. In the second place, it is in the interest of a unified scientific world-view that physics and biology should be reducible to the same basic conceptual system and axioms. Thirdly, the conception of the living organism as a physical system has become so firmly established in working biology and has proved so fruitful in causal explanations of vital activities that any theory of life must attempt to bring itself into line with this conception. And, finally, because we have already become enmeshed with problems which compel us to consider in detail the exact relationship between the concept of directive correlation and the concepts of physics.

One such problem becomes at once evident when we ask how the independence of the consequences of hypothetical variations of a coenetic variable in a directive correlation (cf. § 14), which the focal condition enjoys, differs from the analogous independence of small initial disturbances which is enjoyed by a stable equilibrium state in a physical system. The two cases are analogous and yet essentially different. Consider a physical system in a state of stable equilibrium, e.g. a ball resting in the centre of a hemispherical bowl. The equilibrium position of the ball at some given point of time, say at t_2, may be likened to the focal condition of a directive correlation. For, provided t_2 and t_0 are chosen far enough apart to enable the system to return to equilibrium after a small disturbance, there exist in this case possible finite variations of the system's t_0-state which will leave the t_2-position of the ball unaffected. And, to complete the analogy, it is easy to find two variables whose values at some intermediate point of time t_1 are causally affected by these hypothetical variations; which in turn affect the ball's return to equilibrium; and which are mutually correlated in a manner analogous to directive correlation. For instance, the deviation of the ball from the centre of the bowl at t_1 and the magnitude at t_1 of the restoring force would constitute such a pair of correlated variables.

This analogy has played a confusing part in recent philosophical biology in that it has led a number of biologists to think of the living organism as a material system in constant pursuit of physico-chemical equilibrium. Against this conception others have pointed out that it is just as reasonable to say that the only state of equilibrium an organism can achieve is death, and, therefore, that living organisms may equally well be conceived as material systems which are constantly staving off equilibrium. The strange coexistence of these two dia-metrically opposite points of view in modern biology furnishes a typical example of the confusions which vague and ill-defined concepts can engender.

Another question pointing to the same need for exactitude is that of the probability of events whose occurrence is secured by directively correlated activities. In §§ 8 and 15 it was said that the directive activity of the gun-training mechanism creates an objectively biased incidence of direct hits. The exact nature of this objective bias is a point which requires precise treatment.

The task we have set ourselves requires that, as a working hypothesis, we regard the living organism as a physical system. It also requires, as has already been emphasized in Chapter I, a certain amount of mathematical notation. But this notation will only occur *qualitatively*, i.e. for purposes of exact expression, and *must not be taken to imply any claim on our part that it may prove of computative or prognostic value.* Nor must it be taken to suggest fictitious possibilities of using new quantitative methods in the familiar manner of much pseudo-scientific literature.

For simplicity the physical sciences, and physics itself, have so far been treated in our discussions as if they were a unitary whole and as if physical theory were a single axiomatic system. From a broad methodological point of view this simplification is undoubtedly justified, but now that we are about to para-phrase directive correlation in physical terms we can no longer overlook certain broad divisions which separate different branches of physics. This particularly concerns the distinction between the concepts of modern atomic physics, i.e. the quan-tum physics of atomic dimensions, and the orthodox molar and macroscopic physics, i.e. the physics of matter in bulk and of dimensions which are large compared with those of the elementary particles. It is well known that these two systems of concepts are not inconsistent since the laws of quantum physics asymptotically approach those of the classical macro-scopic physics if averaged over a large system of elementary particles. But we shall, nevertheless, have to make our choice, and in this two considerations will guide us. First, the phenomena to which the biologist currently applies the concept of 'adaptation' and related concepts, even if he classes them as microscopic from a biological point of view, are macroscopic in the physical sense, i.e. in comparison with the dimensions of atomic particles. Secondly, the conceptual apparatus of quantum physics is considerably more cumbersome than the other; and there are further complications. For instance, the quantum conception of elementary particles is no longer capable of visualization; the statements of quantum physics are not primarily statements about observable physical quantities as such, but about the probabilities of observing under such-and-such circumstances such-and-such values of the quantitative variables concerned; and the initial state of a closed physical system is conceived to determine no more than the subsequent development of these probabilities. In consequence, the concept of directive correlation, if defined in terms of quantum physics, would have to undergo a re-examination analogous to that of causation.[1]

All these complications make it evident that the slight gain in generality which would result from a quantum definition of directive correlation would be more than offset by the resulting loss in simplicity and lucidity. In the sequel, therefore, we shall base our discussion on the conceptual system of orthodox macroscopic physics. We shall see that in this classical framework causality can be defined as a certain perfectly straightforward functional relationship between the values possessed by physical variables at distinct points of time, and need not involve us in any of the traditional philosophical controversies about this concept.

§ 17. *Some Fundamental Physical Relations and Definitions*

Physical theory looks at the data of observation from many angles, but the form of physical description and representation

[1] See Appendix.

of physical events which most immediately bears on the present subject of inquiry is that of a closed[1] material system undergoing physical changes in time.

The commonsense notion of such systems is that of an objective situation involving material objects and having both constant and variable characteristics. While the identity of the system is, as it were, preserved by the constancy of the former, the variable characteristics of the system may undergo continuous changes in time and thereby cause the given system to pass through a sequence of successive states.

The theoretical models of the physicist do not in general pretend to offer exact replicas of actual material phenomena. He overtly works with the aid of idealized and simplified conceptual models for which no more can be claimed than that they represent the essentials of a particular material situation —or, at any rate, that it is helpful and for purposes of prediction often sufficient to interpret a given situation in terms of the respective idealized models. Thus he will represent a pendulum simply by a line fixed at one end and having a mass-point at the other.

The commonsense notion of closed material systems passing through successive stages of development has its appropriate counterpart in these idealized models of physical theory. In most physical descriptions we can in fact speak of a material *system* which at any particular instant is in a particular (and usually transient) *state*. In these descriptions the system itself is often qualified by the so-called 'imposed conditions', i.e. by an explicit statement that a certain set of functional relations or numerical values are assumed constantly to be satisfied throughout the episode under consideration. And the current state of the system at any stage of its development is specified by the current values of those physical parameters whose values are not fixed by the imposed conditions. We shall call these free parameters the *state-parameters*[2] of the system. The

---

[1] See below, p. 84.

[2] In physics these are simply called the 'coordinates' of the system but to avoid confusing the non-physicist we shall deviate from this practice.

basic assumption of the classical conception of a physical system is that there exists a set of state-parameters whose current values may, for the purpose of the theory concerned, be taken completely to specify the current state of the system. For instance, in classical mechanics we often deal with a system consisting of an aggregate of discrete material particles and the current state of the system is assumed for all purposes of the theory to be completely specified when the position-coordinates and momentum-coordinates of the particles are given. Again, in thermodynamics we deal with systems whose current state is assumed to be completely specified by the current values of the density, pressure, and temperature.

The states of a macroscopical physical system are generally assumed to be capable of continuous changes in time, and the coherent sequence of these continuous transitions from one state to the next may be called the *natural development* of the system concerned. The state in which a given physical system is assumed to be at the beginning of the time interval which the physicist chooses to investigate and at the beginning of a given natural development, is called the *initial state* of that physical system. For theoretical purposes, of course, any conceivable state of the system may by way of hypothesis be taken as the initial state in order to calculate what natural development would issue from it—provided that the initial values which the state-coordinates are assumed to have, are consistent with the imposed conditions and the assumptions made in defining the system itself. The calculation of what natural development would follow from a given initial state of a physical system, normally takes the form of finding and evaluating mathematical equations which express the current values of the state parameters as mathematical functions of the initial conditions and of the time variable.

For our purposes the state-parameters of a physical system may always be assumed to be finite in number. It is true, in the physics of continua, e.g. in field theory, the parameters specifying the field appear *prima facie* to constitute an infinite set of state-parameters. But we may reduce this case to that of a finite set of parameters by interpreting a field as an abstract rule connecting the values of the field variable at that finite number of locations at which, in a given context, measurements are to be made.

When two variable quantities are so related that the value of one of them depends upon the value of the other, they are said to be *functions* of each other. If one of the variables is supposed to vary arbitrarily it is called the *independent variable*. In the sequel we shall use Greek letters to denote functional relationships and in the standard notation, therefore, $x = \phi(y)$ means that to every value of the independent variable y there corresponds a value of x [y is called the *argument* of the function ϕ]. A function is said to be a *single valued* function if to every value of the independent variable there corresponds one and only one value of the dependent variable. Unless explicit mention is made to the contrary, all unspecified functions discussed in this book will be assumed to be single valued functions.

The idea of a function may be extended to functions of several independent variables. Thus $y = \phi(u, v, w)$ means that to every given set of values of u, v, w—say the set u', v', w'— there corresponds one (and on the above understanding only one) value of y.

If the value of any one of the arguments of a function $\phi(u, v, w)$ changes, e.g. if u changes from u' to $(u'+h)$, this will usually entail a change in the value of ϕ. The *rate* at which the value of ϕ changes in comparison with this change of u [v and w being assumed to remain fixed at v' and w'] is known as the *partial derivative* of ϕ in respect of u at the point (u', v', w'), and is symbolized $\dfrac{\partial \phi}{\partial u}$. It is defined mathematically as the value towards which the quotient

$$\frac{\phi(u'+h, v', w') - \phi(u', v', w')}{h}$$

approaches when the value of h approaches zero while v and w remain fixed at v' and w'. The derivative is said to exist only if the above quotient does in fact approach to a definite value when h is made to approach zero. A necessary condition for this is that ϕ should be continuous at v', w', and in the neighbourhood of u'.

The notion of partial derivative may be illustrated by the following example. The height H above sea level of a hill is normally a single valued function of the longitude x and latitude y of any location on it. At any given point (x', y') on the hill the partial derivative $\dfrac{\partial H}{\partial y}$ then represents the rate of climb of the hill in the meridian plane of the point, while $\dfrac{\partial H}{\partial x}$ denotes its rate of climb in the latitudinal plane.

A given quantity z may be a function of a number of independent variables x_1, x_2,..., x_n, each of which in turn is a function of another set of variables y_1, y_2,..., y_p. It can then be shown that, provided all the relevant partial derivatives exist, the following identities hold good

$$\frac{\partial z}{\partial y_k} = \frac{\partial z}{\partial x_1}\frac{\partial x_1}{\partial y_k} + \frac{\partial z}{\partial x_2}\frac{\partial x_2}{\partial y_k} + \dots + \frac{\partial z}{\partial x_n}\frac{\partial x_n}{\partial y_k},$$

where k stands for any one of the suffixes 1, 2,..., p of the variable y.[1] Using the customary notation for a summation this equality may be written

$$\frac{\partial z}{\partial y_k} = \sum_{i=1}^{n} \frac{\partial z}{\partial x_i}\frac{\partial x_i}{\partial y_k}. \tag{1}$$

If a variable is a function of one or more other variables and if a mathematical formula is known which allows us to calculate the value of the dependent variable from the value(s) of the independent variable(s), we shall say that the respective function is a *determined function*. For instance, the volume of a sphere is a determined function of the radius because we know that the two variables are connected by the formula $V = \frac{4}{3}\pi r^3$. On the other hand, the height of a hill is usually

---

[1] For a proof of these identities the reader is referred to text-books on the Differential Calculus.

an undetermined function of the latitude and longitude of any location on it.

This distinction is very important for the biologist because so many functional relationships which he encounters in the study of life are undetermined. And he must, therefore, be particularly careful not to make assertions about them which tacitly imply that they are determined. For instance, the idea of eliminating a certain variable from two undetermined functions cannot be accepted as meaningful without further explanation. On the other hand, it is equally essential to realize that it is possible to make perfectly accurate and significant scientific statements or hypotheses about functions even when they are undetermined—just as in algebra we can make such statements about undetermined values of variables. Thus it is a perfectly significant statement (which may be either true or false) to predicate of a certain undetermined function that it is continuous or that it has a certain partial derivative. It is a perfectly legitimate statement to predicate that the rate of climb of a certain hill at a certain point is such-and-such even although the function which connects the height with different loci on the hill is undetermined. These observations particularly concern the contents of Chapter **IV**.

For purposes of illustration, and to clear up a number of distinctions to be introduced hereafter, I shall give a simple example showing the typical conception and treatment of a physical system as they occur in the ordinary routine of macroscopic physics.

Consider the flow of water from a vertical tank of uniform and constant cross-section A through an orifice whose cross-section a expands at a uniform rate bt, where t is the time coordinate. If h_0 is the initial height of the water, it is required to express the current height h_t of the water as a function of the time t.

The physical system here consists of the vertical, and partly filled, tank with its expanding orifice, and the theory of this case requires only two state-parameters, viz. h_t and the current cross-section of the orifice, a_t.

The natural development of the second state-parameter is already given by the imposed conditions in terms of which the present physical system is defined, for, if a_0 is the initial cross-section at $t = 0$, we have

$$a_t = a_0 + bt. \tag{2}$$

The natural variation of h_t remains to be calculated, and for this purpose the axioms of geometry and of hydrodynamics provide two appropriate equations. The first is, that for any infinitesimal increment of time dt

$$a_t v\, dt = -A\, dh, \tag{3a}$$

where v is the velocity of outflow of the water. The second is,

$$v = c\sqrt{(2gh)}, \tag{3b}$$

where g is the gravitational constant and c is an empirical constant introduced to correct the oversimplifications made in deriving the expression $\sqrt{(2gh)}$.

If we write B for $c\sqrt{(2g)}$ we get from (2), (3a), and (3b)

$$(a_0 + bt)\, dt = -\frac{A}{B}\frac{dh_t}{\sqrt{h_t}},$$

hence by integration and by inserting the initial conditions as constants of integration,

$$a_0 t + \frac{bt^2}{2} = -\frac{2A}{B}\left(\sqrt{h_t} - \sqrt{h_0}\right)$$

and the required functional relationship between h_t and t is found to be:

$$h_t = \left\{\sqrt{h_0} - \frac{B}{2A}\left(a_0 t + \frac{bt^2}{2}\right)\right\}^2. \tag{4}$$

§ 18. *Causal Connexions*

With this example before us we may now draw a distinction between two types of functional relationships which may exist between the state-parameters of physical systems. For, looking at equation (4) we may say that there are two distinct ways of interpreting this equation and, for that matter, all analogous equations in physics. There are two kinds of information we may obtain from it:

(*a*) In equation (4) a_0 and h_0 may be regarded as 'given' in addition to the constants b, A, and B, while t is regarded as an independent variable. In this way of looking at (4), therefore, the equation is read in a manner which is properly symbolized

$$h_t = \psi(t). \tag{5}$$

This mode of presentation may be called a *time-representation* of our tank-plus-water system, and in representing h_t as a function of the time t it answered the problem set in the preceding section. A time-representation is thus seen to be the proper representation for predicting future physical occurrences from a given state of affairs.

(*b*) As an alternative (although not the only alternative) manner of reading (4), we may regard t, b, A, and B as given, while h_0 and a_0 are regarded as independent variables. And we may investigate how the value of h at any particular point of time, say at t_1, depends on the initial conditions of our system. We obtain an answer to this question if we substitute t_1 for t into equation (4), thus obtaining

$$h_1 = \left\{ \sqrt{h_0} - \frac{B}{2A}\left(a_0 t_1 + \frac{bt_1^2}{2}\right) \right\}^2. \tag{6}$$

Equation (4) in this form, therefore, is read as

$$h_1 = \phi(h_0, a_0), \tag{7}$$

t_1 now playing the part of a constant.

In contrast with the previous type of presentation we may call this a *causal representation* of our tank-plus-water system. It represents the manner in which any particular state of the system depends on the initial state of the system, and, therefore, the manner in which causal connexions enter into the routine of macroscopical physical theory.

For our special purposes causal representations are the most important representations of physical relationships. We have already on two occasions drawn attention to the vagueness of the concept of causality in ordinary discourse and in traditional philosophy. But there is none of this vagueness and complexity about the above functional relationships and for our further purposes we need not understand by a 'causal connexion' anything more than just the above type of functional relationship between the final and initial state of a given physical system. It will therefore be perfectly safe for us in the sequel to employ the terms 'causal', 'causality', 'causal connexion', &c. on the express understanding that they must be taken to refer to no more than just this existence of antecedent physical determinations as arguments in functions relating to subsequent physical determinations.

A causal connexion is therefore defined as follows:

The value at any point of time t_1 of a (set of) state-parameter(s) X is *causally connected* with the value at a prior point of time t_0 of a (set of) state-parameter(s) Y if, in a causal representation of the system, X_{t_1} is a single valued (but not uniformly constant) function of Y_{t_0}.

It is important to note that, according to this interpretation of causality, h_1 in our example is causally connected to h_0 and that, speaking generally, the value which any physical variable has at a particular point of time is causally connected with any of its prior values.

Suppose that in a subsequent mathematical discussion of our example some variable z were to occur which could be represented as a function of h_t, i.e.

$$z_t = \chi(h_t).$$

If we now substitute h_t in this function by the right-hand side of equation (4), the function will become transformed into a new function

$$z_t = \eta(h_0, a_0).$$

We shall call such a transformation a *causal transformation* and the function η will be called a *causal transform* of the function χ.

Returning to interpretation (7) of equation (6), it is seen that this envisages the variations in h_1 which would be entailed by variations in the assumed initial conditions of the system. These variations of the initial conditions are, as we know, purely hypothetical variations and are no part of the natural development of the given physical system. In physical theory such hypothetical variations are called 'virtual variations'. They do not compare different states of the same actual system, but compare the corresponding states of an ensemble of alternatives of the actual system which differ in nothing but their initial states and in whatever consequences this entails for the system's subsequent natural development. For instance, if a set of particles in analytical dynamics is subject to certain imposed conditions, then at any given instant any set of arbitrary small displacements of the particles permitted by the imposed conditions as they apply to that instant, is said to be a set of 'virtual' displacements of the particles for that instant. These virtual displacements depend only on the conditions imposed for that instant and not on the manner in which these conditions may vary with the time. In this respect, therefore, the virtual displacements for the given instant differ fundamentally from the actual or time displacements of the particles. Thus, if we have a physical system consisting of a ball initially at rest on an inclined plane, then the true variation of the ball's position will, of course, be along the line of steepest descent; but a virtual variation of the ball's position is any variation permitted by the constraints of the inclined plane, i.e. any variation in the plane and upwards from it.

Virtual variations represent therefore the same sort of thing in theoretical physics as what in § 7 we have called the 'generating principle of an ensemble'. In the present case the membership of the ensemble is determined by the range of values of a_0 and h_0 over which (7) holds good.

The point to be made is that, in spite of their purely hypothetical character, virtual variations and ensembles are accepted as perfectly legitimate formal elements in the concept-systems of physical theory. Since for the purposes of this book we accept the methods of physics without question, we are entitled to use these formal elements in our later work without need of further justification.

The above definitions of 'causal connexion', 'causal transformation', and 'causal representation' apply not only to determined functions between the values of state-parameters but equally to undetermined functions, i.e. functions for which there exists no known analytical formula enabling the value of the dependent variable to be calculated from those of the independent variable(s). It is, for instance, a perfectly significant and definite statement to assert that to each of a number of possible alternative values of a certain variable in the initial state of a given physical system there corresponds *ceteris paribus* one and only one value of a certain variable in the final state of the system, even when no analytical formula is known for this one-one correspondence.

These are particularly important points to bear in mind in connexion with biological statements. It shows, for instance, that it is a perfectly significant and definite statement— which may, of course, be true *or* false—to say that the movement of a given animal at any time is causally connected with certain prior brain processes, even when the biologist cannot specify any general formula for this one-one correspondence and may even be unable to enumerate all the parameters involved. It is equally legitimate to symbolize such an asserted relationship in ordinary functional notation, provided it is added, or understood from the context, that this symbolic expression is to convey no more than that each process is asserted to represent the natural development of a definite and finite (although not enumerated) number of parameters and that to each set of values which the one set of parameters may be assumed to have at a given instant there corresponds under the prevailing assumptions one set of values at a later instant of the other set of parameters.

According to our definition the concept of 'causal connexion' is strictly applicable to all biological processes, including those of which we know neither all the physical parameters involved nor the analytical form of the functional relationships between them. This must, however, be qualified by the remark that in biological cases, as in ordinary physical cases, the idea of causal connexion as formulated above applies only to *closed* systems. In this work we mean by a 'closed' system a system whose natural development is assumed to be determined by no other factors than those implied or explicitly mentioned in the definition of the system, the imposed conditions, and in the specification of the initial state.[1] A closed physical system, in the present sense, need not therefore be a system which is free from outside influences. It is merely free from *unspecified* outside influences. Nor need it be a system with a constant total energy.

§ 19. *Epistemic Independence*

It is now necessary to introduce a new concept which the reader may not at first find very easy. We have seen that when we think of causal connexions we envisage different possible initial states of the physical system concerned and compare the different natural developments which would result from them in accordance with the fixed assumptions made in defining the system. Thus, in reading equation (6), § 18, in the manner of (7), we imagined a_0 and h_0 to undergo virtual variations and saw that the fixed assumptions of the case implied that h_t was causally connected to both these variables. Now, in the functional relationship (7) we are obviously entitled to regard a_0 and h_0 as independent variables, for it is perfectly consistent with the assumptions of that case to imagine variations of a_0 while h_0 is kept constant and vice versa. Such a situation, however, is not always the case. If we were to write (6) in the following form

$$h_1 = \left\{ \frac{V_0}{A\sqrt{h_0}} - \frac{B}{2A}\left(a_0 t_1 + \frac{bt_1^2}{2}\right)\right\}^2,$$

where V_0 is the initial volume of the water in the tank,[2] we could not treat V_0 and h_0 as independent variables, since $V_0 = Ah_0$ and a variation of either one of these variables without a corresponding variation of the other would violate the fixed assumption made, in defining our system, that A is constant. To distinguish these two cases we shall say that h_0 and a_0 in this physical system are *epistemically independent*,

---

[1] It is important to remember that throughout the remainder of this work the term will be used in this special sense and that it must not be confused with different usages in other branches of science.

[2] And hence $\dfrac{V_0}{Ah_0} = 1$.

whereas h_0 and V_0 are *epistemically dependent*. Hence, epistemic independence may be defined as follows:

A set of state-parameters of a physical system S is a set of *epistemically independent* parameters if the definition and imposed conditions of S, and the physical laws which are assumed to apply to it, admit arbitrary constellations of values of these parameters as possible initial states of S, and hence permit the *initial* values of these parameters to be treated as mutually independent variables.

Since any point of time in the natural development of S may

FIG. 5.

be selected as an initial point of time, it is evident that, according to this definition, a set of state-parameters is epistemically independent if it is such that at any instant the value of no member of the set is determined by the value *at that instant* of one or more other members of the set by reason of the conditions imposed on the system *for that instant*, or of the laws held to apply to it. The clauses 'at that instant' and 'for that instant' are important. For, to recur to our illustration, if we insert equation (2) into (6) for the value $t = t_1$ we obtain h_1 as a function of h_0 and a_1. Thus, although h_1 and a_1 are epistemically independent state-parameters, they may, as the result of certain mathematical operations, nevertheless appear as functions of each other in physical equations. But, as the example illustrates, these functions can be derived only by means of a reference to the natural development of the system and to instants of time other than t_1. In fact, it reflects the presence of factors of joint causation. The joint causal factor here is a_0, the causal connexions being those shown in Fig. 5.

It is important to note that the notion of epistemic independence formulated above is a contingent notion. It specifies a certain independence *only* in relation to a given set of fixed assumptions about the physical system concerned: it is contingent upon our definition of the system.

It may be helpful to conclude this section with one or two further examples.

In the ordinary mechanical conception of a simple pendulum
the deviation of the pendulum from its vertical position and
the magnitude of the restoring force cannot be considered a
pair of epistemically independent state-parameters. For,
according to the prevailing fixed assumptions and the laws
held to apply to it, the value possessed by the one at any given
instant determines the value of the other at the same instant.
On the other hand, the temperature of the pendulum and the
pendulum's deviation from the vertical position are epistemically independent, even although in the development of
the system (i.e. in the course of the pendulum's oscillations) the
former comes to influence the latter. For, given the temperature of the pendulum at any given instant, the deviation at that
instant from a vertical position is not thereby determined.
Hence, arbitrary combinations of deviation and temperature
may be considered as possible initial states of the system,
whereas arbitrary combinations of the deviation and the
restoring force cannot be entertained as initial conditions
without a previous re-definition of the system.

Finally, consider a simple Le Chatelier system consisting of
iodine, hydrogen, and hydrogen iodide. Subject to certain
temperature conditions the reaction

$$H_2 + I_2 \rightleftarrows 2HI$$

is reversible; that is to say, it takes place to some extent in
the direction of both arrows and an equilibrium is finally
established between these two opposing reactions. Le Chatelier's principle tells us that if we add hydrogen alone or iodine
alone to the system, this equilibrium is shifted in the direction
of the upper arrow, and if hydrogen iodide is added it will
shift in the reverse direction. The rates of increase or decrease
of concentration are calculable and the equilibrium is given
by the Law of Mass Action. In this case the three concentrations evidently constitute a set of epistemically independent
state coordinates: the system may be imagined to begin with
any combination of them. But a set of parameters consisting
of the three concentrations plus one or more rates of change

of concentration would not constitute an epistemically independent set since under the given assumptions the value of the former at any instant would determine the value of the latter at the same instant.

§ 20. *A Mathematical Definition of Directive Correlation*

The foregoing preliminaries have served to set the stage for the main task of this work. This is to show how mathematical and precise expressions can be found in terms of which such biological concepts as 'adaptation', 'coordination', 'regulation', 'integration', may be paraphrased in exact terms (whenever the biological or philosophical problems at issue require this) without loss of meaning and in a manner strictly consistent with the conceptual framework and axioms of macroscopic physics. The last requirement will come to be fulfilled by the simple device of constructing our definitions from no other elements than physical variables and those types of functional relationships between them which were discussed in the preceding sections and are part and parcel of classical physical theory.

Our starting-point will be a re-definition of the concept of directive correlation. In the definition to be given below we shall make the simplifying assumption that certain functional relationships between quantitative variables are differentiable, and therefore continuous. On a number of grounds it seems justifiable to begin with this simplifying assumption. In the first place it will enable us to keep our discussion on an easily visualizable level and to use a formalism which conforms to that of elementary physical theory. Secondly, the main implication of the requirement that a function should be differentiable within given intervals of its arguments is that it should be continuous in those intervals. And if we examine the kind of hypothetical variations which we normally envisage when we form the idea of a causal connexion, we find that they are usually continuous variations standing to other variations in a continuous functional relationship. We do not envisage the target in our ballistic example to be capable of traversing a merely finite set of discrete alternative paths, nor the rifleman to be merely capable of aiming in a finite set of discrete directions. A third point is that those functions which enter into the usual physical descriptions of macroscopic systems are in the vast majority of cases continuous and differentiable. Nevertheless, we shall show in § 25 how generalized mathematical definitions of directive correlation can be given which do not depend on any assumptions of differentiability or continuity.

Consider a closed physical system S whose state at any time t is specified by the current values $x_1^t, x_2^t, ..., x_n^t$ of the *epistemically independent* and arbitrarily numbered state-parameters $x_1, x_2, ..., x_n$. Let this closed system undergo a given natural development and let the values which the state-parameters assume during that natural development be called their 'actual' values at the respective instants of time. Also, let this natural development be deterministic so that the value at any time t of any one state-parameter may be expressed as a function of the initial values of the state-parameters, i.e.

$$x_1^t = \eta_1(x_1^{t_0}, x_2^{t_0}, ..., x_n^{t_0}, t-t_0),$$
$$x_2^t = \eta_2(x_1^{t_0}, x_2^{t_0}, ..., x_n^{t_0}, t-t_0),$$
$$\cdot \quad \cdot \quad \cdot \quad \cdot \quad \cdot \quad \cdot \quad \cdot \quad \cdot$$
$$x_n^t = \eta_n(x_1^{t_0}, x_2^{t_0}, ..., x_n^{t_0}, t-t_0). \qquad (8)$$

(Not all the state-parameters need, of course, actually occur as arguments of these functions. They have been inserted merely for symbolic simplification. This can be done since parameters not actually occurring in a function may be imagined to occur with zero coefficients.)

In a manner to be laid down presently, directive correlation between state-parameters may then be defined by means of the following three assumptions:

I. Assume that at a point of time t_1 the conditions

$$\gamma_1(x_1^{t_1}, x_2^{t_1}, ..., x_n^{t_1}) = 0,$$
$$\gamma_2(x_1^{t_1}, x_2^{t_1}, ..., x_n^{t_1}) = 0,$$
$$\cdot \quad \cdot \quad \cdot \quad \cdot \quad \cdot \quad \cdot$$
$$\gamma_p(x_1^{t_1}, x_2^{t_1}, ..., x_n^{t_1}) = 0. \qquad (9)$$

are necessary and sufficient conditions for the subsequent occurrence in the natural development of S of a certain event or state of affairs FC, and that the actual t_1-values of the state-parameters of S fulfil these conditions.[1]

II. Assume that there exist

(i) a certain point of time t_0 prior to t_1,

(ii) a certain state-parameter x_k and an interval $\Delta' x_k$ containing the actual value of x_k at t_0, and that

$$\sum_{i=1}^{n} \frac{\partial \gamma_h}{\partial x_i^{t_1}} \frac{\partial x_i^{t_1}}{\partial x_k^{t_0}} = 0 \qquad (10)$$

for every value of $x_k^{t_0}$ within $\Delta' x_k$ in conjunction with the actual t_0-values of the other state-parameters,[2] and for every value of $h = 1, 2, 3, ..., p$.

It will be noted[3] that the left-hand side of (10) is equivalent to the partial derivative $\dfrac{\partial \gamma_h}{\partial x_k^{t_0}}$ and, hence, that (10) is equivalent to

$$\frac{\partial \gamma_h}{\partial x_k^{t_0}} = 0. \qquad (11)$$

III. Assume that for at least one value of h there are two or more terms in the left-hand sum of (10) which do not vanish and that the numeration of the state-parameters is so arranged that these non-vanishing terms have consecutive values of the suffix i, so that

$$\frac{\partial \gamma_h}{\partial x_i^{t_1}} \frac{\partial x_i^{t_1}}{\partial x_k^{t_0}} \neq 0 \qquad (12)$$

for $i = 1, 2, ..., f$.

If the system properties of S are such that the conditions I–III are fulfilled the values $x_1^{t_1}, x_2^{t_1}, ..., x_f^{t_1}$ of the state-parameters $x_1, x_2, ..., x_f$ will be said to be *directively correlated* in respect of the *focal condition FC* and the *coenetic variable* $x_k^{t_0}$. The greatest interval $\Delta' x_k$ throughout which the assumptions I–III remain valid will be called the *maximum variation* of the coenetic variable $x_k^{t_0}$. It represents the maximum range of permissible

---

[1] $p < n$.

[2] $\dfrac{\partial x_i^{t_1}}{\partial x_k^{t_0}}$ is the derivative of the function η_i in (8) with $t = t_1$.

[3] § 17.

coenetic variation and may be taken as a measure of the *degree* of the directive correlation. Alternative measures are the number of coenetic variables, i.e. the number f, and the number of correlated variables. But, unless mention is made to the contrary, we shall in the sequel understand by the *degree* of a directive correlation its 'maximum variation' and we shall refer to the number of correlated or coenetic variables involved in any directive correlation as the *range* of the correlation.

Subject to the simplifying assumptions made at the beginning of this section, the assumptions I–III and the subsequent definitions represent an exact formulation in physico-mathematical terms of the functional relations which our preliminary analysis of adaptation brought to light and which were embodied in the provisional definition of directive correlation given in § 10. The intrinsic meaning of equation (10) is best realized if we turn to its equivalent form (11). It is then seen to state that the prevailing system-properties of S are such that arbitrary hypothetical variations of the t_0-value of the state-parameter x_k will have no effect on the ultimate occurrence of FC in the natural development of S, provided that these virtual variations remain within the interval $\Delta' x_k$ specified in assumption II. For, if such a virtual variation of $x_k^{t_0}$ be denoted by $\partial x_k^{t_0}$, then (11) yields for any γ_j, where $j = 1, 2, ..., p$,

$$\partial \gamma_j = \frac{\partial \gamma_j}{\partial x_k^{t_0}} \partial x_k^{t_0} = 0$$

and this tells us that these variations of $x_k^{t_0}$ will leave the ultimate occurrence of FC within the natural development of S, and at some point of time subsequent to t_1, unaffected. Meanwhile, III tells us that this happens in spite of the fact that neither $\dfrac{\partial x_i^{t_1}}{\partial x_k^{t_0}}$ nor $\dfrac{\partial \gamma_h}{\partial x_i^{t_1}}$ vanish for $i = 1, 2, ..., f$, i.e. in spite of the fact that the virtual variations of $x_k^{t_0}$ causally entail variations in the t_1-values of the parameters $x_1, x_2, ..., x_f$, and that each of these variations if considered in isolation would have causally affected the subsequent occurrence of FC. That is to say, (10) in conjunction with (12) expresses the

property that the independence of FC from the virtual variations of $x_k^{t_0}$ is due, not to the absence of causal connexions, but
to the mutually offsetting or compensating nature of the partial
effects of the virtual variations in $x_k^{t_0}$. We have here a precise
characterization of the special kind of independence which
exists between the focal condition and the coenetic variable,
and to which attention was drawn in § 14.

Taken in conjunction with the concepts introduced in § 17
this mathematical definition of directive correlation may at
first seem rather complex. In particular, the concept of
adaptation as an instance of directive correlation (viz. when k
has one of the values $1, 2,..., f$) now appears before us as a
composite structure erected from the following principal
ideas:

- (*a*) a closed physical system capable of existing in different
  states, i.e. the idea of a set of imposed conditions involving a number of free variables;
- (*b*) the system undergoing a determined natural development;
- (*c*) epistemic independence of some variables;
- (*d*) functional relations between the values possessed by the
  free variables at the same point of time, and between the
  values possessed at different points of time in a causal
  representation of the system's development;
- (*e*) virtual variations of these variables at at least two
  distinct points of time t_0 and t_1, and of ensembles in
  which these virtual variations are the generating principle;
- (*f*) causal transformations of functions; and
- (*g*) derivatives of functions and derivatives of functions
  of functions.

Complex though this list may be, yet, with the exception of
(*g*), our preliminary analysis has shown these elements in one
form or another definitely to be implied in the biological concept
of adaptation when it refers to the goal-directed character of
vital activities. The degree of this complexity merely goes to
show how important it is to think accurately and to use precise

terms when discussing the general characteristics of life; and how many tacit assumptions may be hidden even in simple statements about these characteristics.

In conclusion it should be noted that the preceding definition of directive correlation does not presuppose any of the functions involved to be 'determined' functions in the sense defined in § 17. All the assertions contained in this definition remain significant if the functions are undetermined. It should also be noted that our definition formally shows directive correlation to be a physical system-property which is fully compatible with the causal description of nature.

§ 21. *Singular and Continuous Directive Correlation*

Directive correlation has so far been defined only for a single instant of time, viz. t_1. If, however, we want to find the most adequate expressions for paraphrasing in exact terms the biological meaning of such concepts as 'adaptation', 'coordination', and others, we may find it practicable to extend our definition of directive correlation to cover finite intervals of time. For instance, if a monkey grabs a banana the movement of its arm is adapted to the position of the banana throughout a finite interval of time. For the complete characterization of such cases it may therefore be desirable to have a definition in which t_1 is replaced by a variable and the respective directive correlation is defined to exist for all values of this time coordinate within a finite interval. There are a number of possible ways of doing this. A very general way, closely conforming to the ideas to be expressed, would be to replace the constant t_1 by a variable τ, and t_0 by $\tau - \zeta(\tau)$, where ζ is a positive single-valued function of τ. It is easy to see what further modifications this requires in the definition given in the preceding section: we must now demand the existence of a finite interval $\Delta\tau$ such that the conditions I–III (with τ substituted for t_1 and $\tau - \zeta(\tau)$ for t_0) hold good for all values of τ which lie within that interval.

A system satisfying these modified conditions could be said to show a *continuous directive correlation* between the values possessed by the state-parameters $x_1, x_2, ..., x_f$ throughout the time interval $\Delta\tau$ and we may distinguish this case from our original case by referring to the original one as a *singular* directive correlation. A continuous directive correlation obviously becomes a singular one for $\tau = t_1 =$ constant. The special case in which $\zeta(\tau) = C$, where C is a constant, may be called a *uniform* directive correlation. A uniform directive correlation would exist, therefore, between two variables x and y if, for any value of t within a certain finite interval Δt, x_t and y_t are directively correlated in respect of the same focal condition and if these individual directive correlations all have their coenetic variables at a point of time which precedes t by a constant amount.

According to the definition suggested above a continuous directive correlation consists of an infinite set of singular directive correlations all of whose members refer to the same focal condition. This conception was introduced in order to express the relationships which prevail when a continuous sequence of animal movements or organic states is directed towards a single ultimate 'goal'. But all these definitions are merely given to illustrate how the various purposive phenomena in nature *can* be given precise formulations and the reader will find no difficulty in constructing alternative definitions to bring out particular aspects of such purposive phenomena. The importance of elasticity in the definition of scientific concepts has already been stressed in § 5 and our present aim is not to suggest one and only one way in which the meaning of, say, 'adaptation' can be paraphrased in exact terms. Our aim is merely to illustrate along what lines this goal can be reached and how the present approach allows a great variety of different shades of meaning of such concepts as 'adaptation' to find accurate formulation.

It should also be remembered that we do not intend to translate the whole language of biology into physico-mathematical terms, but merely to show how such terms can be made available for the precise discussion of a specific problem or for tracing all the implications of a particular biological assertion, whenever the intricacy of the questions at issue calls for the greatest possible precision.

§ 22. *A Worked Illustration of Singular Directive Correlation*

The functional relationships in nature which are most characteristic of life are usually too complex to allow all the functions which might be relevant in any particular case to be determined. One of the main problems of the biologist is, as we know, to make significant and definite assertions about such undetermined functional relationships, and he must be careful not to assume tacitly that they are determined. Our definition of directive correlation was drawn up with this requirement in mind. To follow up our definition with a simple worked illustration using determined functions it will therefore be more practicable to fall back on an inorganic case. The ballistic example of our earlier analysis provides a convenient example.

A further consideration has influenced this particular choice. When, in developing a theory, a scientist creates *ex hypothesi* a complex set of formal conditions, he takes upon himself the onus of showing that something exists which satisfies those conditions. For our purposes it is particularly important to show that the conditions envisaged in our mathematical definition of directive correlation can be fulfilled by an inorganic system. In broad outline we know already that our automatic gun when in working order satisfies directive correlations, but it will nevertheless be instructive to illustrate in detail what formal conditions our defining requirements I–III, § 20, impose upon the gun and its controlling machinery.

Before we proceed to apply our definition of directive correlation to this concrete example it is necessary to stress the fact that, since we are at present merely engaged in the business of constructing, clarifying, and testing physico-mathematical concepts which promise to be of heuristic value in the discussion and interpretation of organic behaviour, the reader must not expect this worked example to lead to any equations of practical value in ballistics. The ballistics expert is concerned with the special problem of predicting the future position of a target from an incomplete set of data. He has developed his own theoretical method for solving this problem, based on the probability calculus and the theory of stochastic processes. Often he has also acquired the confusing habit of speaking of the target's motion as if it were intrinsically indeterministic, whereas in actual fact the case is merely that some of its determining factors are subjectively undeterminable by the gunner or the gun-predictor. But none of these things concerns us here. Our problem is semantic and not practical. *The reader who believes that a statistical approach could assist in the solution of our present problem has misunderstood the fundamental nature of that problem.*

For simplicity let our example be constructed on the primitive assumptions that the target travels with constant velocity in a straight line during the reaction lag of the gun and the time of flight of the projectile, and that the projectile also travels with constant velocity in a straight line.

We may regard the gun plus the gun-training apparatus plus the relevant domain of the environment containing the target as a closed macroscopical physical system undergoing a determined development. Let this system be called G and let the initial time be t_0, it being for simplicity assumed that the gun-predictor obtains all its information concerning the target at that instant of time.

Graphically we can set out the whole system in the plane which passes through the target's course and the gun's position. On the strength of our assumptions this plane will then also contain the path of the shell (see Fig. 6).

Let the speeds of the target and projectile be denoted by u and v respectively, and AB denote the path of the target. In the above diagram assume the gun to be situated at the origin O of a cartesian coordinate system whose axes x and y are coplanar with AB and let the target be in the position T_1 at the time of firing, t_1. Allowing for the finite velocity of the projectile the gun will have to aim ahead of the target by an angle $\widehat{T_1 O T_t}$, where T_t is the position of the target at the time when it is struck by the projectile. Let the position-coordinates of the target and of the projectile be denoted by X, Y and x, y respectively, while the angle between AB and the x-axis is designated β. Finally, assume that the whole system G goes through a given natural development in which the target is hit by a shot which was adapted to the target's course.

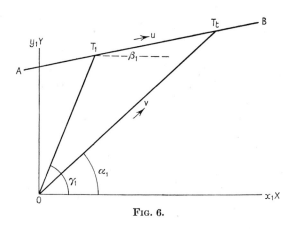

FIG. 6.

Our present requirement is to paraphrase the idea that the gun's line of fire is *adapted* to the target's course, in terms of definite equations. Now there are several parameters which enter into the description of the target's path and to which the gun's line of fire may be said to be adapted. For our purposes it will be sufficient to consider only one such adaptive relationship. Let this be in respect of the angles β_1 and γ_1, i.e. the values of β and γ at t_1. Our task, therefore, is to express in mathematical equations the assertion that the angle α_1 is directively correlated to the set of variables β_1 and γ_1, in respect of the focal condition of a direct hit and in respect of the coenetic variables β_0 and γ_0.

As a suitable set of epistemically independent state-parameters of G we may take α and β, together with the position-coordinates of the target. That is to say, our definition of G leaves us free to imagine any arbitrary combination of

H

these four parameters as its initial state—u and v being assumed given by the definition.

In terms of these assumptions the equations (9)–(12), § 20 may be illustrated as follows:

The focal condition is the occurrence of an impact between the projectile and the target at some time t subsequent to t_1, i.e.

$$\left.\begin{array}{l} x_t - X_t = 0, \\ y_t - Y_t = 0. \end{array}\right\}$$

Simple geometrical considerations show that these equations may be causally transformed into two equations connecting the t_1-values of the chosen parameters,

$$v(t-t_1)\cos\alpha_1 = OT_1\cos\gamma_1 + u(t-t_1)\cos\beta_1,$$
$$v(t-t_1)\sin\alpha_1 = OT_1\sin\gamma_1 + u(t-t_1)\sin\beta_1.$$

From these two equations the factor $(t-t_1)$ may be eliminated, which yields the equation

$$\frac{\cos\gamma_1}{v\cos\alpha_1 - u\cos\beta_1} = \frac{\sin\gamma_1}{v\sin\alpha_1 - u\sin\beta_1}$$

and, hence,

$$\Phi(\alpha_1, \beta_1, \gamma_1) \equiv v\sin(\gamma_1-\alpha_1) - u\sin(\gamma_1-\beta_1) = 0$$

as the analogue of (9), § 20.

According to I, II, and III, § 20, therefore, the assertion that the gun's line of fire is *adapted* to β_1 and γ_1, may be paraphrased by the precise assertion that the gun-training mechanism works in such a manner that there exist finite intervals $\Delta'\beta_0$ and $\Delta'\gamma_0$ containing the actual value of β_0 and γ_0 respectively, such that for all values of β_0 within $\Delta'\beta_0$

$$\frac{\partial\Phi}{\partial\alpha_1}\frac{\partial\alpha_1}{\partial\beta_0} + \frac{\partial\Phi}{\partial\beta_1}\frac{\partial\beta_1}{\partial\beta_0} + \frac{\partial\Phi}{\partial\gamma_1}\frac{\partial\gamma_1}{\partial\beta_0} = 0, \tag{13}$$

and for all values of γ_0 within $\Delta'\gamma_0$

$$\frac{\partial\Phi}{\partial\alpha_1}\frac{\partial\alpha_1}{\partial\gamma_0} + \frac{\partial\Phi}{\partial\beta_1}\frac{\partial\beta_1}{\partial\gamma_0} + \frac{\partial\Phi}{\partial\gamma_1}\frac{\partial\gamma_1}{\partial\gamma_0} = 0, \tag{14}$$

and that at least the first and the second term in (13) and the first and the third term in (14) do not vanish.

§ 23. *Directive Correlation and Physical Stability*

Absolute stable systems are physical systems which are stable compared with states differing from a given state not only by infinitesimal amounts but also in respect of finite differences. The equilibrium shape of elastic solids is a typical example; a simple pendulum at rest is another.

In § 16 we gave an illustration of the kind of problem that crops up in a discussion of the precise meaning of adaptation by pointing to the analogy which exists between directive correlation and certain relations prevailing in physical systems whose state is one of absolute stable equilibrium. It was stressed at the time that in spite of this analogy there exists a crucial difference. We are now sufficiently equipped to specify the exact nature of this difference.

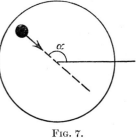

Fig. 7.

In physical terms the analogy between behaviour showing directive correlation and the behaviour of physical systems in a state of absolute stable equilibrium is the following. If we have a material system in absolute stable equilibrium, we know that finite virtual variations in the initial state of the system will set up restoring forces which will eventually re-establish the state of equilibrium. Take the example cited in § 16, viz. the ball inside a hemispherical bowl, and consider in a horizontal projection of this system the relation between the polar angle α of the ball's displacement from the centre of the bowl and the polar angle β of the restoring force (Fig. 7).

It is a necessary condition for the ball's return to equilibrium that the restoring force acts in a direction opposite to the displacement of the ball from its equilibrium position, i.e. that $\beta = \alpha + 180°$. Now, if the ball is displaced from the centre at an initial point of time t_0 and returns at a subsequent point of time t_2 the values of α and β will at any time in the intervening interval automatically fulfil the conditions I–III, § 20,

i.e. the conditions of directive correlation, with the return of
the ball to equilibrium as a focal condition; with α_0 as a
coenetic variable; and with

$$\beta - \alpha - 180 = 0,$$

$$\frac{\partial \beta_1}{\partial \alpha_0} - \frac{\partial \alpha_1}{\partial \alpha_0} = 0,$$

as the analogues of (9) and (10) respectively.

So much about the analogy between physical stability and
directive correlation. Let us now consider the difference. This
is that α and β are epistemically *dependent* state-parameters
whereas our definition of directive correlation expressly
demanded that the correlated state-parameters should be
epistemically *independent*; α and β are epistemically dependent
because, owing to the physical laws held to be valid in the
present case, the direction of the ball's deviation from the
centre of the bowl at any instant determines the direction of
the restoring force for the same instant.

Similarly, in an elastic solid we have a physical system in
which the stress tensors and strain tensors fulfil conditions
analogous to those of directively correlated variables, with the
initial degree of the distortion of the solid from its equilibrium
shape as coenetic variable and with the return of the solid to
that shape as focal condition. But here again, the two tensors
are not epistemically independent.

The comparison between directive correlation and physical
stability may therefore be put as follows: the traditional theory
of physical equilibria specifies the general conditions which
certain epistemically *dependent* variables of a given physical
system must fulfil if in some given respect the final state of the
system is to be independent of initial disturbances. Directive
correlation, on the other hand, specifies the conditions which
epistemically *independent* variables of a system must fulfil if
a similar independence of the system's final state from initial
disturbances is to prevail.

The reader may at first fail to appreciate the fundamental
importance of this distinction, but the point is this: the type

of correlation between epistemically dependent variables which in the case of physical stability leads to the restoration of a disturbed stable equilibrium and which was illustrated by the correlation between α and β in the preceding example, does not require the existence of a coenetic variable. *It does not require joint causation.* Directive correlation, on the other hand, *does* require joint causation (§ 9), and in each case, therefore, requires a certain minimum set of causal connexions (cf. Fig. 3).

It will be recalled that the necessity for joint causation in directive correlation arises in the following way: the concept of directive correlation denotes the existence of a certain type of functional relationship between the simultaneous values of a number of epistemically independent state-parameters, viz. functional relations which are defined in terms of the subsequent occurrence of a certain event or condition in the course of the system's natural development. But since the parameters concerned are *ex hypothesi* epistemically independent, and since, therefore, the value of any one of them at any instant cannot be determined by the values of the others at the same instant, the only possible way in which this functional relationship can come about is for those parameter values to be determined by prior parameter values in the manner of joint causation.

At this point the following objection may occur to the reader: Suppose we have an automatic gun of the type assumed in § 22 and suppose the gun's line of fire is again adapted to the target's course, and hence equations (13) and (14), § 22, satisfied, would it not then be possible simply to pronounce (13) and (14) as laws of nature (viz. laws concerning certain types of specially conditioned automatic guns)? And would not this render the gun's line of fire and the target's path epistemically dependent, thereby removing the necessity of a coenetic variable?

This objection would be valid if the distinction between epistemic dependence and epistemic independence were an absolute distinction. But, as has been pointed out, it is only a relative distinction in that it classifies the state-parameters of a physical system only in relation to a given set of fixed assumptions. Moreover, it is an integral part of the concept of a physical system that it should be capable of existing in different states. Hence, every physical system has at least one degree of freedom and, in the vast majority of cases, several degrees. With very rare exceptions, therefore, every physical system will contain several epistemically independent parameters. In actual fact, the very nature of scientific method sets a limit to the number of epistemically independent state-parameters which could be reduced to epistemic dependence by the above sleight of hand, because with every such reduction the system conceived would become one degree less abstract and the class of its possible realizations would be reduced by one dimension. And if scientific theory is denied access to sufficiently high levels of abstraction and generalization, its very method of axiomatization becomes impossible. Science would become a mere inventory of unique events.

Directive correlation is at the root of the distinguishing characteristics of observed life, and the characteristic independence of environmental fluctuations which living organisms enjoy is primarily of the type that protects the focal condition of a directive correlation from variations of the coenetic variables. It is the confusion between independence through directive correlation and independence through physical stability which has led so many biologists to think of living organisms merely as 'systems perpetually tending towards equilibrium', 'large molecules', 'aperiodic crystals', 'physical gestalten', &c. Von Bertalanffy's concept of 'aequifinality'[1] misses the point for the same reason. Our analysis has shown that these confusions are largely based on a failure to distinguish between epistemically dependent and independent variables.

§ 24. *Directive Correlation and Probability*

In our preliminary analysis adaptive behaviour was described as behaviour which involves an objectively biased occurrence of appropriateness, and it was contrasted with accidentally

---

[1] *Naturwissenschaften*, 1940.

appropriate behaviour. Since these are probability statements the question is raised as to the exact relation between directive correlation and probability. The question is also important because the distinction between random processes and purposive processes plays an axiomatic part in several statistical theories. We are reminded, for instance, of Maxwell's imaginary little demons whose purposive behaviour leads to exceptions to the Second Law of Thermodynamics.

Unfortunately, there exists no generally accepted definition of 'probability' which could be taken as a starting-point in our examination of the relation between this concept and that of directive correlation. First of all, therefore, we must try to find a satisfactory definition of probability.

If one considers a number of possible future events which are such that one of them must occur to the exclusion of the others, it often happens that we expect one of them to occur rather than another, and in the fundamental meaning of the word an event would be called more or less 'probable' according to the degree of this expectation. With the work of Fermat and Pascal a gradual refinement of this original meaning of probability set in, which allowed the concept to be represented by a mathematical quantity. The classical formula to which this development led was the following: Given a state of affairs in which a finite number A of future events are equally possible, one of which must occur to the exclusion of the others and B of which are regarded as favourable, then the probability p that the actually occurring event will be a favourable one is defined as

$$p = \frac{B}{A}.$$

To-day this so-called *a priori* formula is usually rejected as a satisfactory definition of probability, because, it is said, 'equally possible' can here only mean 'equally probable'; hence, the definition already presupposes the concept of 'probability' and is circular. Yet, in all the examples traditionally used to exemplify and test this *a priori* formula, such as the spinning of coins, the throwing of dice, &c., the meaning of 'equally possible' was intuitively so certain that this shortcoming of the classical definition of probability did not prevent the mathematical properties of the number p from being carefully investigated. The results of these investigations are embodied in the modern theory of mathematical probability.

A number of well-known attempts have been made to find alternative definitions of probability which would not be circular. James Bernoulli and Laplace, for instance, tried to meet the difficulty by invoking the principle of insufficient reason. They suggested that events are 'equally possible' because we are equally uncertain about them; that is to say, because after taking into consideration all relevant evidence one of them cannot be expected in preference to another. But this interpretation is obscure. It also leads to certain unsatisfactory conclusions. For instance, if a bag contains black and white balls the probability for one who did not know in what proportions these colours were represented would always be 1:2 of picking a white ball, even if there was only one white ball among a thousand black ones.

Already among the earliest uses of the term 'probability' we find it applied not only to things that are likely to happen, but also to things that are likely to be true, to propositions. The best known formal development of this interpretation is J. M. Keynes's theory, in which probability is regarded as the 'degree of our rational belief' in the truth of a proposition. The main drawback of this interpretation is that it cannot satisfactorily be cast into numerical terms. It also fails, therefore, to offer a solution of the difficulty.

The third well-known line of approach takes the idea of 'relative frequency' as a starting-point. Reduced to fundamentals the idea of this school of thought is to define the probability of, say a 'six' falling in the throw of a die as

$$\lim_{n \to \infty} \frac{m}{n},$$

where m is the number of 'sixes' thrown and n the total

number of throws in a given series of trials. This definition, however, shows a number of logical defects which it has not so far appeared possible to remove, even in the carefully elaborated form in which the theory was given by von Mises and Reichenbach.

The failure of these attempts to provide satisfactory alternatives to the original *a priori* theory of probability, suggests the question whether the latter cannot be modified and refined in a way which avoids presupposing the idea of 'equally possible' or 'equally probable' events, while at the same time avoiding the idea of 'insufficient reason'. This does not seem too difficult, and the interpretation of probability which I shall develop and adopt below is only a few steps removed from several modern attempts to define probability along *a priori* lines.

The definition of probability which I shall propose is based on the following provisional assumptions:

Suppose we have a physical system S which is so specified that within the terms of the specification it can only have as initial state one of a set Q of n alternative states $Q_1, Q_2, ..., Q_n$; and suppose that we want to know which of these possible initial states will cause a certain event E to happen in the course of the subsequent development of S—physical determinism being assumed throughout. Now we may be lucky and by deduction or experiment acquire all the desired knowledge. In other words, we may succeed in discovering which individual members of Q will entail the subsequent occurrence of E and which will not. On the other hand, we may be only partly successful and acquire only incomplete information about the question. Among the several possibilities of such incomplete knowledge one stands out as being particularly important. This is the case in which we can infer from symmetry considerations or statistical evidence that a certain fraction m/n, say one-quarter, of the possible initial states of S will lead to the subsequent occurrence of E while the remainder will not, *without*, however, being able to say *which* individual initial states belong to this fraction and which do not.

It is to this type of incomplete information that I shall confine the meaning of 'probability'; viz. I propose to say by way of provisional definition that, in the above case, the probability of E occurring as the result of any particular initial state Q_1 is equal to the fraction m/n.

To give a simple example, if we think of a person spinning a coin with a certain precisely specified movement of the hand, and if the specification leaves nothing open except whether the coin at the beginning of the spinning movement lies 'heads' upwards or 'tails' upwards in the operator's hand, we then have in the hand-plus-coin-plus-table a physical system which is restricted to two possible[1] initial states. We know of these two initial states that if the one causes 'heads' to turn up then the other must cause 'tails' to turn up. For they differ in nothing that could affect the movements of the coin from the moment that it was being spun until the moment when it came to rest. But *ex hypothesi* we do not know beforehand *which* initial state will result in *which* side of the coin turning up at the end of the operation. According to our definition, therefore, the probability that a throw satisfying the assumed specifications will yield 'heads' or 'tails' is $1:2$.

In one respect the provisional assumptions from which we started are artificial and unnecessarily restrictive. For we do not usually think of situations such as the throwing of dice or the spinning of coins as specified so precisely that the specification allows only a finite number of alternative initial states. As understood normally there are an infinite number of possible ways of 'spinning a coin' or 'throwing dice'; and in most conceptions of physical systems of this kind the initial state has a continuous range of possible variations and the number of possible initial states of the systems is infinite. Our next task, therefore, must be to drop these artificial assumptions and to extend our definition in a way which will allow it to be applied to physical systems having an infinite set of permitted initial states.

The difficulty here is that this can be done only if we can

---

[1] i.e. compatible with the definition and specification of the system.

assume the infinite set of initial states in principle to be measurable. Otherwise it would be meaningless to speak of 'finite fractions' of the set. Fortunately, modern mathematics has been able to develop formal devices for measuring infinite sets which meet the requirements of our theory. Some infinite sets can be measured by ordinary measuring operations. For instance, the measure of the infinite set of points contained in a finite interval (a, b) of a line is simply the quantity $b-a$. But modern mathematics has been able to define extremely generalized formal measures, e.g. the 'Lebesque Measure', which enable sets of elements to be assigned a measure number also when normal operations of measuring do not apply. There is no need to go into the technicalities of these devices. For our purposes it is sufficient to know that adequate formal 'measures' exist for all the infinite sets that may concern us here.

This enables us now to drop the original restriction of our definition of probability to systems which are specified so precisely that they have a merely finite number of alternative initial states, and we may restate our definition in the following generalized form:

If in a physical system S

  (i) Q is the (finite *or* infinite) set of all initial states which are compatible with the definition and specification of the system, and is 'measurable';[1]

 (ii) R is the measurable set of all members of Q which cause a certain event E to occur in the subsequent development of S;

(iii) it is not known which particular members of Q are also members of R and which are not;

(iv) the relative measure of R, i.e. the quotient of the measure of R over the measure of Q, is a known fraction m/n;

then the *probability* that any given member of Q will entail the subsequent occurrence of E in the natural development of S is m/n.

---

[1] In the formal sense mentioned above.

We may take a throw of a die as a convenient illustration. In our ordinary conception of such an operation the throwing movement is not specified in detail and the operator's hand together with the die and the table may be regarded as a physical system having an infinite number of possible initial states. This infinite set of initial states may be assumed to be 'measurable' in the formal mathematical sense of the preceding remarks. Next, symmetry considerations tell us at once that this infinite set may be exhaustively divided into six mutually exclusive subsets of exactly equal measure such that all the members of any one subset, but no two members of different subsets, will cause the same number on the die to turn up at the end of the throw. For to every particular throwing movement in conjunction with a particular initial position of the body of the die in the hand, there correspond 24 possible initial states of the system according to the 24 possible arrangements of the faces of the die in that physical position. And these 24 possible arrangements are obviously divisible into 6 groups of 4 arrangements each, such that all members of the same group, but no two members belonging to different groups, cause the same number on the die to turn up at the end of the throw.[1] Finally, it is also true that we do not know which initial position of the die, arrangement of the faces, and throwing movement will cause which number to turn up at the end of the throw. All the conditions laid down in our definition of probability are therefore fulfilled and the probability that any particular number of the die will turn up is seen to be 1:6.

The definition of probability we have just put forward has all the intuitive advantages of the classical *a priori* definition yet, unlike the latter, it does *not* presuppose the idea of 'equally probable' events and avoids, therefore, the charge of being circular. It makes no assumptions about the likelihood of the initial states of S, i.e. of the members of the set Q. In

---

[1] Each group consists of the four possible arrangements in which the number that will turn up at the end of the throw occupies the same initial position.

fact, the concept of probability as here defined cannot be applied to the individual members of Q at all, for it is only defined for the *effects* of initial states of the system and cannot therefore be applied to the initial states themselves.

Our definition also avoids the difficulty which Bernoulli and Laplace incurred when they interpreted 'equally possible' to mean 'equally uncertain'. In the first place we avoid the vagueness of that interpretation, and, secondly, we avoid the difficulty of the black and white balls. If a man picks a ball from a bag containing one white ball among a thousand black ones and does not know in what proportion they are represented, the interpretation of Bernoulli and Laplace, as we know, makes the probability of picking a white ball equal $1:2$. According to our definition the probability is $1:1001$, irrespective of whether he knows this proportion or not. The question is merely whether that proportion of black to white balls is included in the specification of the system consisting of the operator, the bag, and the balls.

We are now in a position to clarify the relation between probability and directive correlation.

To this end consider a physical system in which the t_1-values of a number of state-parameters $x_1, x_2, ..., x_f$ are directively correlated in respect of a certain focal condition FC, and let the t_0-value of a parameter x_k be the coenetic variable. Now assume that the initial state of the system is so precisely specified that the t_0-values of all state-parameters are completely determined, except those of x_k. Of this variable the specification only demands that its value at t_0 shall lie within certain finite limits x_k' and x_k'' respectively. Finally assume that the degree of the directive correlation is known, i.e. the magnitude, M, of the maximum variation; also that it is not known which values of $x_k^{t_0}$ will cause FC and which will not.

In that case it is clear that, according to the above definition of probability, the *degree* of the directive correlation, viz. the magnitude M, determines a minimum value for the probability that any particular value of $x_k^{t_0}$ will cause the event FC.

For, according to our definition, this probability cannot be less than

$$\frac{M}{x'_k - x''_k}.$$

In other words, in any conception of a physical system in which the specifications of the system leave only the coenetic variables undetermined, *the degree of a directive correlation determines a value below which the probability that the focal condition will occur cannot drop.*

An important biological implication of this result is the following: In any conception of an organism and its environment in which only the coenetic variables of the adaptation are regarded as undetermined variables, the degree of the organism's adaptation[1] to its environment determines a minimum value for the probability of its survival.

§ 25. *A Generalized Definition of Directive Correlation*

The definition of directive correlation given in § 20 assumes that the state-parameters $x_1, x_2, ..., x_f$ and x_k have a continuous field of variation and that the functions $\gamma_1, ..., \gamma_f$ and $m_1, ..., m_f$ are differentiable. Our reasons for these assumptions were given at the time. They were partly heuristic and partly based on the desire to give a definition which would be in line with the formalism of classical physics. In the present section an illustration will be given of how directive correlation may be defined without making such restrictive assumptions and how, therefore, the concept may be extended to variables having a discontinuous field of variation or variables which are confined to a finite set of discrete values.

This will allow the idea of directive correlation to be applied to two important cases not covered by our earlier definition. The first case is that of biological variables which refer to integral numbers, such as the number of legs, segments, eyes of an insect. In the second place we shall be able to apply the idea to those complex properties of living organisms which are

---

[1] The notion of 'adaptation' being here of course restricted to adaptation having the survival of the organism as focal condition.

not measurable in the usual sense but for which there exist
nevertheless accurate procedures for ascertaining whether they
are fulfilled in any particular case. I am thinking of such
properties as 'being a lion', 'being carnivorous', &c. If required,
such properties can be treated mathematically by the familiar
device of introducing a numerical variable which is simply
defined to have (say) the value 1 if the animal has the respective property and the value 0 if it has not. For instance, we
may introduce three variables x, y, and z, and define that
$x = 1$ denotes the property of being an amphibian, $y = 1$ the
property of having a tail, and $z = 1$ that of having legs, while
the zero-values of the respective variables denote the absence
of these properties. On the strength of these definitions the
Apoda would then be characterized by $x = 1$, $y = 1$, $z = 0$;
the Urodela by $x = 1$, $y = 1$, $z = 1$; the Anura by $x = 1$, $y = 0$,
$z = 1$. However, the point to be made is merely that as soon
as a mathematical concept becomes applicable to variables
which are confined to a finite set of discrete values, it can be
applied to complex properties of the kind we have just
illustrated.

In the definition of directive correlation we are about to give
neither the coenetic variables nor the directively correlated
variables need have a continuous field of variation, and the
admissible range of coenetic variation may have either a finite
or infinite set of values.[1]

Consider again a closed physical system S whose current
state is specified by the current values of n state-parameters
$x_1, x_2, ..., x_n$, and let the following apply to this system:

1. With t_0 assumed to be the initial time

   (a) let A be a set of possible initial states of S whose
   members are distinguishable by the values of a single
   parameter or index λ;

   (b) let $\bar{\lambda}$ denote any value of λ belonging to a member of
   A and let $A(\bar{\lambda})$ denote the member having that value;

---

[1] No new principle will be introduced by this generalized definition and the
reader who takes no particular interest in these formal details may omit the
remainder of this section.

(c) let $x_k^{t_1}(\bar{\lambda})$ denote the t_1-value of the state-parameter x_k in that natural development of S which begins with the initial state $A(\bar{\lambda})$.

2. With t_1 instead of t_0 assumed to be the initial time of S

(a) let B denote the set of all possible initial (t_1) states of S;

(b) let Q denote a certain event or state of affairs, and let C be the set of all those members of B which will cause Q to happen in the subsequent natural development of S.

Next, assume that

I. The set A has more than one member.

II. Every t_1-state of S which results from a member of the set A is a member of C.

III. The state-parameters of S can be so numerated that there exists a set $x_1, x_2,..., x_f$ of state-parameters, where $f > 1$, such that for every value of $j = 1, 2,..., f$ and any value $\bar{\lambda}'$ of $\bar{\lambda}$,

  (i) $x_j^{t_1}(\bar{\lambda}') = x_j^{t_1}(\bar{\lambda}'')$ only if $\bar{\lambda}' = \bar{\lambda}''$,

  (ii) there exists at least one value $\bar{\lambda}''$ different from $\bar{\lambda}'$ for which the t_1-state $x_1^{t_1}(\bar{\lambda}'), x_2^{t_1}(\bar{\lambda}'),..., x_j^{t_1}(\bar{\lambda}''),..., x_n^{t_1}(\bar{\lambda}')$ is a member of B,

  (iii) but there exists no value $\bar{\lambda}''$ different from $\bar{\lambda}'$ for which this state is also a member of C.

We shall then say by way of definition that the values $x_1^{t_1}(\bar{\lambda}'), x_2^{t_1}(\bar{\lambda}'),..., x_f^{t_1}(\bar{\lambda}')$ are *directively correlated* in respect of the focal condition Q and the *coenetic variable* $A(\bar{\lambda})$. The admissible range of coenetic variation is given by the largest set A for which the above assumptions hold good. Its measure represents the *maximum variation* of the directive correlation.

Although the formalism employed in this definition differs greatly from that employed in § 20, it expresses the same fundamental ideas. Assumption (I) establishes $A(\bar{\lambda})$ as a variable; (II) implies that every value of this variable within the admissible range of coenetic variation will entail the occurrence of Q; and (III) expresses again the basic principle of directive correlation, viz. that only a set of suitably 'geared' values of the variables $x_1^{t_1}, x_2^{t_1}, ..., x_f^{t_1}$ will bring about the subsequent occurrence of Q and that, within the limits laid down, hypothetical variations of the coenetic variable will have only suitably 'geared' variations of $x_1^{t_1}, x_2^{t_1}, ..., x_f^{t_1}$ as their consequence.

IV

APPLICATION TO CHARACTERISTIC
BIOLOGICAL PHENOMENA

§ 26. *Preliminary Remarks*

In the interests of clarity many of the foregoing discussions have centred around simple inorganic examples. As the next step towards an analysis and clarification of the general nature of life, we must now pass to a number of biological applications of the concept of directive correlation, and show how this may serve to clarify the distinctive purpose-like character of life processes. In § 6 it was seen that the concept of adaptation is the main generative element in the more complex concepts in terms of which the various manifestations of this purpose-like character are commonly thought of, e.g. 'coordination', 'regulation', 'integration', &c. Having learnt how to express the meaning of 'adaptation' in mathematical terms, we hold in the concept of 'directive correlation' the key for the explication of these more complex concepts as well. For a science as confused in its general theories as biology, the supreme importance of reaching this level of precision in the discussion of the general nature of observed life has already been emphasized and requires no further comment, except the reminder that our present purposes are entirely analytical. No claim is made that the results of this analysis will in any direct sense benefit the working biologist in the technical execution of his practical problems. Our aim is to understand the general nature of life in rigorous scientific terms, and practical considerations are therefore merely of secondary importance. But in so far as the practical work in any science must, to some extent, be guided and inspired by theoretical and abstract conceptions, it would be equally wrong to assume that the results of our analysis are irrelevant to practical biology.

The main difficulty we are up against in approaching the rather more complex biological concepts is that these, even more than the concept of adaptation, are currently used in several different shades of meaning. We shall approach this difficulty in much the same spirit as in the case of adaptation, and select those meanings which refer to the most characteristic qualities of life processes. For instance, in referring to vital activities the word 'coordination' may stand merely for a functional dependence between certain biological variables. But when the biologist talks about the characteristic muscular 'coordination' involved in animal movements he usually means a good deal more. For one thing, he means that the respective muscular excitations appear to be integrated in some functionally effective and purposeful manner. In this instance, therefore, we shall concentrate on the latter meaning of 'coordination' and ignore the former. Even so, no useful purpose would be served by cataloguing all concepts current in biology which somehow refer to some purpose-like aspect of life processes. Now that we possess in the concept of directive correlation a new conceptual instrument to deal with the phenomena of life, many of the older concepts retain little more than a broad guiding function and with this exhaust their heuristic value.

Every explication of a concept is at the same time an interpretation of it and, in so far as the interpretation enables us to incorporate the phenomenon concerned into a consistent and comprehensive system of theoretical thought, also an explanation. Some of the following sections will therefore have a predominantly analytical character while others will appear to be more of the nature of interpretations and explanations of actual phenomena.

By way of working hypothesis, we shall continue to think of a living organism as a physical system whose macroscopic developments are subject to causal determination. The fact that the concept of directive correlation enables us to express the purposive character of life processes in terms consistent with this hypothesis, incidentally removes an important reason for considering alternative hypotheses.

The following examples have been chosen to illustrate

typical aspects of observed life on which the results of our analysis will shed new light. Once they are understood the reader should have no difficulty in clarifying the exact relations involved in any of the characteristic vital phenomena surveyed in § 4 by analogous methods.

Although they may appear disconnected, the following sections form a continuous sequence in which we shall try to clarify in turn all the most distinctive characteristics of observed life, thus building up gradually a comprehensive picture of the physico-mathematical relations which underlie these phenomena.

§ 27. *Adaptive Behaviour*

Our first illustration will be of the general manner in which the concept of directive correlation enables us, when required, to paraphrase statements about adaptive behaviour in precise mathematical terms.

Consider a simple case of animal behaviour which is adapted to current environmental circumstances, for instance the action of a bird pecking at a grain on the ground. In our everyday language we would say that the movement of its head was *adapted* to the position of the grain on the ground and that the goal of the bird's behaviour was to bring the beak into contact with the grain.

Our preliminary analysis of adaptation showed the objective system-property of the bird-plus-grain system which underlies the typically purposive character of the pecking action to be the following: the bird, when pecking, is objectively so conditioned that if the grain had occupied any alternative position on the ground within a certain neighbourhood of its actual position, so that a modified head movement would have been required, then this modification would have in fact occurred. Our further analysis showed that this notion of adaptation requires at least four causally related elements and that it can be made precise with the aid of the concept of directive correlation. It was seen in § 13 that adaptation between two parameters may be regarded as a directive correla-

tion in which the coenetic parameter is identical with one of
the directively correlated parameters, viz. the one *to* which the
other is said to be adapted. Only, it must be remembered that
the value of that parameter which acts as coenetic variable is
an earlier one than the value which acts as directively correlated variable. The present case is evidently one of 'continuous' directive correlation (§ 21) and if the reaction lag of
the bird's muscular responses to its current sense impressions
is constant, then it is also a 'uniform' one.

If x, y, z and X, Y, Z denote the position-coordinates of the
grain and of the bird's beak respectively, and if the pecking
action begins at t_0 and terminates at t, the adaptive character
of this action may be expressed as follows: For any τ which
satisfies $t_0 < \tau < t$, the set of variables X_τ, Y_τ, Z_τ stands in
a continuous directive correlation to the set of variables
x_τ, y_τ, z_τ in respect of the focal condition

$$\left.\begin{array}{l} x_t - X_t = 0, \\ y_t - Y_t = 0, \\ z_t - Z_t = 0, \end{array}\right\} \tag{15}$$

and in respect of the coenetic variable $x_{\tau-r}, y_{\tau-r},$ or $z_{\tau-r}$.[1] And,
as we know, this is a statement which the definitions of § 20
and § 21 enable us to translate into precise mathematical
statements concerning the existence of certain types of functional relationships between certain state-parameters of the
bird-grain system.

These mathematical statements will be of the following
type:

'The bird-grain system is objectively so conditioned that, if
in a causal representation of the system,

$$\phi_1(x_\tau, X_\tau, ..., t-\tau) = 0,$$
$$\phi_2(x_\tau, X_\tau, ..., t-\tau) = 0, \tag{16}$$
$$\phi_3(x_\tau, X_\tau, ..., t-\tau) = 0$$

---

[1] Where r is the reaction lag of the bird.

are the causal transforms of (15) for the point of time τ, and if

$$\gamma_1(x_\tau, X_\tau, ...) = 0,$$
$$\gamma_2(x_\tau, X_\tau, ...) = 0 \tag{17}$$

are the necessary and sufficient conditions that (for values of the state-parameters which lie within the imposed limits) the equations (16) will have a positive and finite solution for $(t-\tau)$, then

$$\frac{\partial\gamma_i}{\partial x_\tau}\frac{\partial x_\tau}{\partial x_{\tau-r}} + \frac{\partial\gamma_i}{\partial X_\tau}\frac{\partial X_\tau}{\partial x_{\tau-r}} + ... = 0,$$

$$. \quad . \quad . \quad . \quad . \quad . \quad . \quad . \quad .$$

and

$$\frac{\partial\gamma_i}{\partial x_\tau}\frac{\partial x_\tau}{\partial x_{\tau-r}} \neq 0,$$

$$\frac{\partial\gamma_i}{\partial X_\tau}\frac{\partial X_\tau}{\partial x_{\tau-r}} \neq 0,$$

$$. \quad . \quad . \quad . \quad . \quad .$$

for $i = 1$ and $i = 2$.'

Owing to the complexity of the bird as a living organism and the number of factors which determine its behaviour, it is obviously impossible in practice to enumerate all the physical parameters which enter into the causal determination of the pecking movement and, for instance, cause the bird to peck at all. Even when the physical parameters are known, we do not know the exact relations between them. Hence the functions of (16) and (17) will in practice always be *undetermined* functions. Whereas this naturally rules out the possibility of using our equations for the purpose of predicting with certainty any part of the bird's behaviour, it does not diminish their value for analysis as exact expressions of the adaptive character of the bird's pecking movement and as a means to trace mathematically all essential implications of the assertion that the pecking movement of the bird was an adapted one. This was all we set out to achieve. The reader will recall that the definition of directive correlation given in § 20 does not presuppose the functions involved to be determined functions. It is also worth recalling at this point that directive correlation specifies a *physical* system-property whose reality is not lessened by the fact that it is defined in terms of hypothetical variations of an actual situation.

The above formulation of the purpose-like character of the bird's behaviour does not, of course, bring out the fact that this behaviour is a compound action whose organic unity lies in the coordination and integration of its constituent muscular activity. That aspect of the action will be dealt with in § 31 and § 33.

§ 28. *Phylogenetic Adaptation and Natural Selection*

The next illustration will be of the way in which the possibility of paraphrasing in precise terms statements about adaptation, in this case phylogenetic adaptation, may help to solve difficult theoretical questions.

Take the theoretical question whether the purposive and creative character of evolution is compatible with that part of the modern theory of evolution which, on the face of it, seems to be the very antithesis of purposiveness, viz. the haphazardness of gene mutations and their capricious insignificance to the organism's needs. We shall use cryptic coloration as a suitable instance of a phylogenetic adaptation with a marked appearance of purposiveness.

For simplicity, consider a population of butterflies whose caterpillars are individually monochromatic, although there may be variations of colour throughout the population. Assume also that the habitat of the population is monochromatic throughout. Let the larval coloration of the species be cryptic in the sense that a given statistical average of the colours of its members, say the modal colour, is the same as the colour of the habitat. Let both these colours be assumed variable in time and let their current shades be denoted by the wave-numbers P_t and Q_t respectively.

Our first task is to express the adaptive character of the caterpillars' colour in exact terms. Now, cryptic coloration presents a case of adaptation whose focal condition is concealment. Our state-parameters in the present conception are the colour P_t of the species and the colour Q_t of its habitat. They are also the directively correlated variables. On our assumptions the necessary and sufficient condition at any time t_1 for concealment to occur is that $P_{t_1} = Q_{t_1}$. Hence, if for simplicity we concentrate at present only on such a single instant of time, the equations (9) here take the form of the single equation

$$\gamma(P_{t_1}, Q_{t_1}) \equiv P_{t_1} - Q_{t_1} = 0. \tag{18}$$

If the population-plus-habitat system throughout the evolutionary episode be regarded in a causal representation and as a closed system whose natural development starts at time t_0, our equations (10) yield the following equation as a mathematical expression for the *adaptive* character of the caterpillars' colour (it being understood that neither term of the sum vanishes)

$$\frac{\partial \gamma}{\partial P_{t_1}} \frac{\partial P_{t_1}}{\partial Q_{t_0}} + \frac{\partial \gamma}{\partial Q_{t_1}} \frac{\partial Q_{t_1}}{\partial Q_{t_0}} = 0. \tag{19}$$

Since it follows from (18) that

$$\frac{\partial \gamma}{\partial P_{t_1}} = 1 \quad \text{and} \quad \frac{\partial \gamma}{\partial Q_{t_1}} = -1,$$

(19) reduces to
$$\frac{\partial P_{t_1}}{\partial Q_{t_0}} - \frac{\partial Q_{t_1}}{\partial Q_{t_0}} = 0$$

or
$$\frac{\partial P_{t_1}}{\partial Q_{t_0}} = \frac{\partial Q_{t_1}}{\partial Q_{t_0}}. \tag{20}$$

According to our analysis, therefore, the statement that the modal colour of the caterpillars at any particular point of time t_1 is adapted to the colour of the habitat, implies in the main that there exists at least one point of time t_0 prior to t_1 such that in a causal representation of the development from $t_0 - t_1$ the derivative of the function which expresses the causal connexion between the colour of the species at t_1 and that of the habitat at t_0 is the same as that which expresses the causal connexion between the colour of the habitat at t_1 and its colour at t_0.[1] It is obvious that for this to be true in the case

[1] The meaning of $\partial Q_{t_1}/\partial Q_{t_0}$ must not be confused with that of $\partial Q_t/\partial t$. The former expresses how Q_{t_1} would have differed if Q_{t_0} had been different, while the latter expresses the rate at which Q changes with the time at t. Suppose $\partial Q_t/\partial t = c$, where c is a constant, then $Q_{t_1} = Q_{t_0} + c(t_1 - t_0)$ and, therefore, $\partial Q_{t_1}/\partial Q_{t_0} = 1$.

of phylogenetic adaptation the interval $(t_1 - t_0)$ must be large enough to allow finite evolutionary changes in the gene composition of the population to take place.

If the colour of the environment is assumed to change in any fashion that may be expressed in the form

$$Q_t = Q_0 + \int_0^t \Phi \, dt,$$

where Φ is a function of variables which are independent of Q_0, then (20) reduces to

$$\frac{\partial P_{t_1}}{\partial Q_{t_0}} = 1. \tag{21}$$

We conclude from this analysis that the theory of natural selection is compatible with the purpose-like character of the adaptive evolution of the colour of our caterpillars, provided that there are mechanisms which allow the equations (20) or (21) to be satisfied.

According to the modern theory of particulate inheritance three major factors determine the evolutionary change of P_t, since the latter obviously depends on the distribution and frequency of the various colour determining genes and their allelomorphs in the population:

i. Mutation pressure; that is to say, the feeding of some allele x, y, or z, into the population by spontaneous recurrent mutations;

ii. The so-called 'scattering of variability'; e.g. chance disappearance from the population of alleles which are present in very small proportions. This may have a cumulative effect in small populations.

iii. Natural selection, in this case the selective elimination of the less protected caterpillars.

Of these three possibilities, (i) could render P_{t_1} a function of prior values of Q in spite of the assumed haphazardness of mutations if the mutation rate itself were to depend on the colour of the habitat; but since we have no evidence that mutation rates depend on wave numbers in the visible spectrum we may ignore this possibility; (ii) cannot render

P_{t_1} a function of any Q_{t_0} because the very notion of a chance disappearance of alleles precludes this possibility; but (iii) obviously does render P_{t_1} a function of Q_{t_0} for any suitable t_0, since the rate at which colour variants will be eliminated or promoted by natural selection will depend on the current difference between the colour of the variant and that of the habitat.

We conclude that the theory of natural selection permits the existence of mechanisms which allow (20) or (21) to be satisfied and that it is, therefore, compatible with the purpose-like character of this case of evolution.

§ 29. *Ontogenetic Adaptation*

As a third illustration of how the relations involved in adaptation may be analysed in precise terms, let us take a case of ontogenetic adaptation, that is to say, of the gradual adaptive modifications which an individual organism or its habits may undergo in response to its environment and experience. Also let us take a case which compels us to use the generalized definition of directive correlation given in § 25 rather than the special one given in § 20. Imagine the case of a bird in whose habitat there occur both edible and inedible caterpillars and assume that these are distinguishable by certain external characteristics; for instance, let the edible caterpillars be of a certain 'phenotype' *A*, and the inedible of a 'phenotype' *B*. Assume also that although caterpillars are an important part of its diet the bird is nevertheless at birth incapable of distinguishing the edible from the inedible, and acquires the habit of accepting the '*A*'-types while rejecting the '*B*'-types, only through experience. This habit, therefore, is an *ontogenetic* adaptation.

From our point of view an essential part of the idea of this particular adaptation is that it envisages an environment which has alternative properties so far as concerns the relation between the external appearance of the caterpillars and their edibility. These properties of the environment are regarded as variables. For what hypothetical variations of these variables can the adaptation of the feeding habits of the bird be said to hold good? In any actual case, of course, only empirical evidence can give a complete answer to this question; but, barring special assumptions, common sense suggests a number of possible variations straight away. For instance, we can safely assume that if our bird had been reared in an environment in which the 'A'-type caterpillar was *in*edible and the 'B'-type was edible, it would have developed converse habits, viz. those of accepting the 'B'-types and rejecting the 'A'-types. Let us confine ourselves to this particular hypothetical variation of the environment as an illustration. Any other coenetic variation could be treated on the same lines.

To find an exact expression for this particular ontogenetic adaptation of the bird's habits to the peculiarities of its environment let us introduce two variables y and z, the first referring to the environment of the bird, the second to its habits. Let these variables be defined as follows: y has the value 1 in any environment which contains both edible and inedible caterpillars and in which the former are distinguished by the characteristics A while the latter have the characteristics B; it has the value 2 in any environment in which a similar situation prevails except that the 'A'-type is inedible and the 'B'-type edible; finally, it has the value 0 in any environment in which neither of these conditions is fulfilled. The variable z, too, has by definition only three values. It has the value 1 if the bird has the habit of accepting the 'A'-type caterpillars and rejecting the 'B'-types, the value 2 if the bird has the converse habit, and the value 0 if it has neither of these habits. Since these two variables refer to physical facts which are, in principle at least, ascertainable by experimental procedures, they may be regarded as physical variables and as state-parameters in a physical description of the bird-plus-environment system. Assume that it takes the bird two months to acquire the habit of selecting the right kind of caterpillar. The adaptation of the bird's habits to its environment may then be expressed in the following precise terms: in a causal representation of the bird and its environment as a closed physical system in which y and z are among the state-para-meters, t_0 being the initial time and y being assumed to be constant in time, the value of z_t is directively correlated to the value of y_t for all values of t for which $(t-t_0)$ is greater than two months. The coenetic variable is y_{t_0}; the focal condition is the absence of 'caterpillar poisoning' in the bird.

Since y and z are by definition restricted to a finite set of discrete values, 'directively correlated' must here be under-stood in the sense of the generalized definition given in § 25. That definition yields the present case if Q is taken to denote the absence of 'caterpillar poisoning' in the birds; $x_1^{t_1}$ and $x_2^{t_1}$ are replaced by y_t and z_t; the set A consists of the actual initial state of the bird-plus-environment system (in which $y = 1$) and the hypothetical alternative in which $y = 2$; an imposed condition being throughout that y is constant in time.

§ 30. *Short-, Medium-, and Long-Term Directive Correlations*

The examples of biological adaptation discussed in the last three sections differ in one particularly important respect: in the magnitude of the interval (t_1-t_0), that is to say, the magnitude of the time-slice which separates the coenetic variable from the directively correlated variables. In the first case, that of the bird pecking at the grain, we were concerned with adaptive responses to current environmental circum-stances. The interval (t_1-t_0) was of the order of the reaction time of the bird's sensory and motor apparatus, and it comprised only an insignificant fraction of the life-history of the bird. We shall hereafter call adaptations in which, as in this case, (t_1-t_0) is merely of the order of reaction time, *immediate* adaptations. The respective type of directive correlation will be designated as '*short-term directive correlation*'. To this type, therefore, belong all those purpose-like actions which are usually classed as 'responses', also muscular coordinations, purpose-like physiological reactions and any other quick adjustment which an animal or plant can make to current events or conditions in the environment.

In phylogenetic adaptation, as in the case illustrated in § 28, we have the opposite extreme. Far from being merely an insignificant fraction of the life-history of the animal, the interval (t_1-t_0) here actually exceeds that life history and extends over a significant fraction of the evolution of the species. For in any phylogenetic adaptation the interval between the coenetic variable and the directively correlated variables must be large enough to permit finite evolutionary changes to take effect in the population. Consider again the phylogenetic adaptation of the colouring of the caterpillars and assume for simplicity that the colour Q of their environment is constant in time, so that in the appropriate causal representation of the system any hypothetical variations of Q_{t_0} will imply an equal variation of Q_{t_1}. The concept of 'phylogenetic adaptation' in this case presupposes that (t_1-t_0) is large enough for natural selection to cause a finite hypothetical variation of Q_{t_0} to imply as great a variation of P_{t_1} as of Q_{t_1}. The question whether a physical system contains directive correlation depends therefore largely on the magnitude of the time-slice of its natural development which is taken into account. To avoid ambiguity in biological discussions the magnitude of that time-slice must be clearly understood from the context. The same applies to the *degree* of directive correlation. In our phylogenetic example it is obvious that, barring special assumptions such as the fixation of relevant genes, the farther back in the evolution of the species we fix t_0, the greater will be those hypothetical variations of Q_{t_0} of which we can assume that owing to the effect of natural selection they would be followed by as great a variation of P_{t_1} as of Q_{t_1}. The greater the interval (t_1-t_0), therefore, the greater as a rule will be the degree of the adaptation of P_{t_1} to Q_{t_1}.

The fact that both the existence and the degree of a directive correlation may depend on the magnitude of the time-slice which is taken into account, makes it particularly important to distinguish between the three types of adaptation which have occupied us in the preceding three sections. All directive correlations which are of the type involved in phylogenetic adaptation and have no coenetic variable except if the interval (t_1-t_0) is large enough to permit finite evolutionary changes to take place in the population, will be designated as *long-term directive correlations*. This leaves ontogenetic adaptations as *medium-term directive correlations*. In these the interval (t_1-t_0) lies within the life history of the individual organism but differs from the case of short-term directive correlation in that it comprises a significant portion of that life-history.

Very often a biological situation may derive its purpose-like character from all three types of directive correlations simultaneously and it is important to realize that this may lead to confusion unless the directively correlated variables and coenetic variables of each type are carefully separated. If a bird pecks at a certain caterpillar selected as edible on the strength of its external characteristics, this pecking action itself involves several short-term directive correlations; the acquired habit of selecting the respective type of caterpillar is based on a medium-term directive correlation; and the bird's ability to acquire this habit is based on a long-term directive correlation. When expressed in precise terms each of these directive correlations refers to a different set of correlated variables, different coenetic variables, different causal representations of the bird-plus-habitat as a closed physical system, different ensembles and different time-slices in the development of the system. Our analysis shows, therefore, the many points on which confusion can arise in the discussion of such mixed cases. It also shows, however, the power of our new concepts to sort out the complicated relations which may contribute to the purposive character of biological processes.

§ 31. *The Coordination of Vital Activities*

In many life processes a given biological effect is achieved by the coordinated activities of a number of morphologically distinct organs. A few illustrations were given in § 4 and the phenomenon is pertinent to our inquiry because of the familiar impression of purposiveness which such activities give: 'anticipatory coordination' was the expression we quoted at the time.

The dictionary definition of the verb 'to coordinate' is 'to bring parts into proper relation', and, on the whole, it seems correct to say that the distinguishing characteristic of coordinated biological activities, such as coordinated muscular movements, is that throughout the duration of the movement the participating muscular excitations or inhibitions keep a mutual relation proper to the attainment of a certain biological effect, usually called the 'goal' of the activity. However, in what would seem to be the most characteristic biological sense, this proper mutual relatedness of the muscular activities does not merely mean a mutual appropriateness; it consists rather, of mutual adaptation and 'team-work'. This 'team-work' is not quite that of a team of horses pulling the same way, but rather that of a football team in which each player takes account of the current positions and movements of the others in deciding upon the particular nature of his own current contribution to the game and to the achievement of their common purpose. This 'team-work' quality is particularly characteristic of life processes and it is this meaning of 'coordination' which we shall attempt to explicate. As already mentioned, 'coordination' is also used in other senses in biology, but they are all quite simple and none of them refer to the purpose-like quality of life processes. In the present context they may therefore be ignored.

There are sufficient clues to achieve a precise definition of 'coordination' in the 'team-work' sense without difficulty.

In the first place, to say that the 'coordinated' activities are performed by separate organs may be taken to imply a degree of independence between those activities, which we can identify with epistemic independence (§ 19). Next, to say that the coordinated activities appear to be 'mutually adapted' in relation to a common purpose, clearly means that they are directively correlated to one another with respect to a joint focal condition. And the further statement that each single one of the coordinated activities appears to 'take account of' some of the others in making its own contribution to the realization of this purpose, may be translated into the statement (already implied by the idea of mutual adaptation) that the coordinated activities enter this system of directive correlations not only as correlated variables but also as coenetic variables. For, speaking on the most general terms, it means that the organism is at the time objectively so conditioned that:

(a) to any one given member A of the set of coordinated activities there corresponds a finite range of hypothetical variations in the development of at least one other, B; and

(b) if B had varied within this range in such a way that only a correlated modification of A could have achieved the focal condition, then this modification would in fact have occurred.

Coordination in the 'team work' sense may therefore be defined as follows: a set of activities are *coordinated* if they are directively correlated to one another, and if each activity also plays the part of a coenetic variable in at least one of these directive correlations.

It is worth pointing out that since this definition is reducible to mathematical relations between quantitative variables it shows coordination, in the biological sense, to be a *physical* property. It should also be noted that coordinations need not be based only on short-term directive correlations as in the preceding example, but may also be based on medium-term coordinations such as in many morphogenetic processes.

One of the most important results of our early discussion of directive correlation was that it showed every case of purpose-like behaviour to require a certain minimum number of causal connexions. This will help us to see one particular anatomical feature of higher living organisms in a new biological perspective. I mean the immense complexity of their nervous systems. In the case of coordinated activities the number of causal connexions required is particularly large. To get a rough idea of that number, let us call any set of coordinated activities a case of *perfect* coordination if each of these activities 'takes account of' *all* the others. By way of illustration consider a simple animal movement involving the coordinated activities of four separate muscles M_1, M_2, M_3, and M_4. Let this be 'perfect' coordination in that the current excitation or inhibition of each muscle 'takes account of' the state of excitation or inhibition of each one of the others. Let the state of excitation or inhibition of these muscles be denoted by the variables e_1, e_2, e_3, and e_4 respectively, and let FC be the focal condition of this muscular coordination. If we assume for simplicity that the reaction time r of each muscle in taking account of any of the others is constant, and the same for all, we have here a uniform directive correlation which for any particular point of time t_1 throughout its existence requires the following causal connexions.[1]

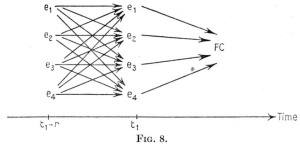

Fig. 8.

In this highly simplified case, therefore, at least twenty causal connexions are required in all, and for a perfectly co-ordinated system of n muscles the number would be at least n^2+n. In actual fact it would be larger because what, for simplicity, we have treated as single variables will usually be a complex set of variables; also, we have merely considered the internal adjustments of the animal movement and not the adaptation to environmental circumstances which it may possess in addition.

This illustration shows how very great the number of causal connexions must be which the extensive coordinations and adaptations of vital activities in the organism require. We may

---

[1] Cf. § 9.

regard *nerve systems* as the special morphological machinery which living organisms have developed to make this multitude of causal connexions possible on a permanent basis and without mutual interference. These systems provide the narrowly canalized and permanent avenues of communication which enable a physical variable in one region of the body to become a causal function of an appropriate physical variable in another region without these causal connexions interfering unduly with the freedom (epistemic independence) of the interposed parts and organs. The (n^2+n)-relation explains the striking increase in the complexity of nervous systems which has accompanied the evolution of higher organisms.

The working biologist differs from the philosophical biologist in that he usually prefers to have the explanation of a biological phenomenon in specific rather than general terms whereas the latter seeks to understand life on higher levels of abstraction and generalization. Thus, whereas the working biologist may want to know the 'proximate cause' of the death of a particular animal, the philosopher may be more interested to know why most higher organisms are mortal. Similarly, whereas the former may be content to know the specific function of, and selective advantage bestowed by, the nerve systems of specific organisms, the latter may seek the rationale of nerve systems in more general terms, and will be best pleased if he can derive the need for such systems from the very definition of life. We can now attempt such a general formulation of the fundamental role of nerve systems: it is to provide a permanent structural foundation for the multitude of independent causal connexions required by the complex directive correlations on which the survival of higher organisms depends.

Unaware of the true nature of the organizational relationships in living systems, a number of scientists have come to regard a living organism as in no essential way different from a complex and 'aperiodic' crystal, 'crystalloid', or giant molecule. Our general formula for the function of nervous systems brings out the fallacy of this view. However complex they may be, mere crystals and molecules require no nervous organization, no organizational machinery at all, because, unlike living organisms, their existence does not depend on directive correlations. They do not therefore require a certain minimum number of independent causal connexions.

These particular theories, therefore, leave the entire organizational apparatus and coordinating organs of living organisms unexplained. They fail to offer a formal reason why there should not exist an organism every bit as adaptive as Man

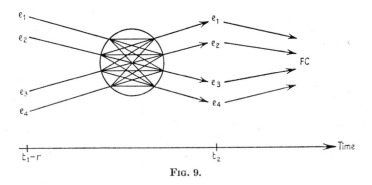

Fig. 9.

and capable of high degrees of coordination, but entirely lacking in nervous systems or other transmissive organizational machinery.

In the case of our hypothetical example the sixteen causal connexions between the coenetic and directively correlated variables (Fig. 8) will be established in the animal by the combined machinery of the afferent kinaesthetic nerves and optical nerves (both of which can inform the central nerve system of the current positions of the limbs) in conjunction with the efferent nerves which relay impulses from the central nerve system to the muscles. The advantage of centralization and the function of nerve centres becomes at once obvious if we look again at the sixteen causal connexions on the left-hand side of Fig. 8. For the existence of a nerve centre enables these causal connexions to be established in a manner which may be symbolized as in Fig. 9 where the circle represents the happenings within the nerve centre. The sixteenfold connectivity now being confined to the connexions inside the nerve centre, only the fourfold afferent and a fourfold efferent connectivity are required outside it. In this manner the greatest possible economy is achieved in the length of the required channels of communication.

§ 32. *The Regulation of Physiological Variables*

After the foregoing discussion of adaptation and coordination little space is needed to clarify the exact spatio-temporal relationships and modes of causal connexion which underlie the various phenomena of biological 'regulation', and to outline the most important senses in which the term 'regulation' refers to the characteristic purposiveness of life processes.[1]

We may first turn to homeostasis, the regulated constancy of the *milieu interne* of living organisms. We know that the proper functioning of most living organisms requires the constancy of certain physiological variables, such as hydrogen ion concentration, temperature, osmotic pressure, &c., in different parts of the organism, and in most of these cases physiological mechanisms are provided in the organism for regulating these variables. The processes of regulation take the form of restorative physiological changes which come into action whenever external or internal disturbances have caused the regulated variables to deviate from the value required by the body, and whose magnitude is usually adapted to the magnitude and direction of the deviation. This correlation between the disturbed variable and the physiological processes effecting the restoration of the *status quo*, is not the same as that existing between the disturbances of a physical system in stable equilibrium and the correlated restorative forces. For, in the latter case, the restorative forces are epistemically dependent on the disturbed variables. In homeostasis, on the other hand, the physical variables involved in the physiological processes that restore the original value of a regulated

---

[1] This excludes, for instance, the sense in which regulation refers to 'gearing' processes or 'master' reactions, when the rate of a sequence of physiological processes is governed by the rate of the slowest term.

variable are, as a rule, epistemically independent of that variable.

The nature of this difference was discussed in § 19 and § 23. To recapitulate this point, take a simple pendulum as an example of a physical system in a state of equilibrium. Any deviation of the pendulum from its vertical equilibrium position sets up a restorative force whose magnitude is epistemically dependent on the magnitude of the deviation: the value of the latter at any given instant determines the value of the former for the same instant, and arbitrary combinations of these two variables cannot, therefore, be considered as possible initial states without altering the fixed assumptions made in describing the system.

By contrast, consider the regulation of the carbon dioxide concentration of the blood through appropriate variations in the rate of pulmonary activity. A deviation of the carbon dioxide concentration above its normal value evokes a change in the rate of pulmonary activity tending to reduce the deviation, but the rate of pulmonary activity and the carbon dioxide concentration are nevertheless epistemically independent. The latter determines the former only for a subsequent point of time and not for the same instant, and there is nothing in the living organism to prevent us assuming (within obvious limits, of course) the existence of any arbitrary combination of carbon dioxide concentration in the blood and pulmonary activity as the initial state of a given span of a man's life.

It is easy to see what type of correlation does exist between the physiological variables and the processes that regulate them. If the carbon dioxide concentration of the blood deviates from its required value, the regulating physiological processes which come into play may evidently be said to 'adapt' the rate of pulmonary activity to the requirement of restoring the carbon dioxide concentration in the blood to its required value. We are therefore dealing with a uniform directive correlation in which the carbon dioxide concentration in the blood and the rate of pulmonary activity at any given instant are the correlated variables, in which the focal condition is the attainment of the required carbon dioxide concentration at a subsequent instant, and in which the coenetic variable is the carbon dioxide concentration at a point of time which precedes the given instant by the reaction lag of this regulative mechanism. All these relations may be given an exact mathematical formulation with the aid of either of the mathematical definitions of directive correlation given in Chapter III.

A number of physiological regulations are one-way regulations. In these cases a physiological variable may not exceed a certain value but may fall below it, or vice versa. The regulation of the carbon dioxide concentration in the blood is such a one-way regulation. The concentration is allowed to fall below a certain value but not to rise above it. This one-way character may be clarified without difficulty, using the exact terminology which we have developed for the discussion of directive correlation: we have just seen that the regulation of a physiological variable involves a directive correlation in which the actual value of the variable at any time plays the part of the coenetic variable and the maintenance of the required value plays the part of a focal condition. If this required value happens to lie within that interval of the coenetic variable which is known to us as the 'maximum variation' of the directive correlation, we have a two-way regulation. Because in that case the physiological variable will be restored to the required value when it deviates in either direction. If, on the other hand, the required value lies outside the maximum variation or coincides with one of its limits, we have a regulation of the one-way type.

In a second important sense in which the term 'regulation' is used the regulating processes do not maintain the regulated variable at a constant value, but at a 'normal' value which may itself undergo more or less rapid changes in time. Instead of a restoration of the *status quo* we have a mere restoration of normality. For instance, in the growing embryo a number of morphological processes follow a 'normal' development and each of these processes is regulated to follow the norm. The concept of a 'normal' development is a rather hazy one.

Sometimes, for instance, biologists will call a biological process 'normal' if it follows a certain familiar course; sometimes if it yields a certain familiar result irrespective of the course it follows; and sometimes only if, in addition, it yields this result otherwise than accidentally, i.e. if it displays apparent purposiveness in advancing towards this result. However, each of these conceptions can be made precise in terms of directive correlation.

In the first case the regulating processes are evidently correlated to the regulated processes by a continuous directive correlation whose focal condition is that the values of the regulated variables should at any time equal the values of the corresponding variables in the given 'normal' development. In other words, the focal condition will be a certain prescribed function of the time or developmental age. In the second case we have a directive correlation whose focal condition consists of the occurrence of the 'normal' result. In the third case we usually have a rather more complex form of directive correlation which will be clarified in §§ 34 and 35.

Between them the different meanings of regulation illustrated here appear adequate in one form or another to describe in exact terms, and hence to clarify, the full range of regulative phenomena outlined in § 4—or, at any rate, to indicate the general nature of the exact spatio-temporal relationships underlying their apparent purposiveness.

§ 33. *Organic Integration: The Organism as Biological Unit*

In an earlier chapter we referred in passing to *biological integration* as the manner in which the innumerable adaptive, regulative, and coordinative processes in living matter are dovetailed, and combine to unite the component parts and 'part-events' of living systems into actively self-maintaining, self-regulating, and reproducing organic wholes, into living individuals.

In a broad sense all instances of adaptation, regulation, coordination, or other organizational relationships, may be called 'integrative' since each directive correlation constitutes a connective relationship which enables us to grasp as a unit or whole what otherwise might appear to be no more than a set of disconnected elements. Apart from any other features they may have in common, any set of objects whose states or activities are directively correlated may be thought of as a unit by virtue of their joint partnership in this single system property, and particularly on the strength of their joint relation to a single focal condition. We thus get the conception of a set of objects which are united by the common goal of their activities. For instance, over and above any contingent unity which they may possess on the strength of other common characteristics, the members of a football team are united by the coordination of their activities during a match and, in particular, by the existence of common focal conditions for these coordinations, i.e. by the existence of common purposes.

It is in this sense that we may describe the football team as 'a whole which is more than the sum of its parts'. That is to say, there are objective relationships (here the physical relationships of directive correlation) between its members which invite us to think of the team as a single unit. And this unit is more than the sum of its parts in the sense that its description requires not only a catalogue of the parts but also an explicit mention of these connective relationships, of these directive correlations.

In the same specific sense we may think of a living organism as a whole which is more than the sum of its parts. For a living organism is a physical system whose parts and activities are connected by a complex and ramified set of directive correlations which, over and above any proximate focal condition, are united by one ultimate focal condition embracing the service of all the main structures and activities of the organism: that of self-preservation. The existence of this all-embracing system of directive correlations with its ultimate focal condition of self-preservation is what unites the parts of an organism into a *biological unit*. This, therefore, is the fundamental meaning of biological integration; and the fundamental characteristic of a living organism is that it is a physical system of mechanically connected parts whose states and activities are integrated by a system of directive correlations of the above kind.

Any connective relationship between a set of elements can be thought of as uniting these elements into a whole. A set of physical objects can be regarded as a mechanical whole if they are mechanically connected, as a geometrical whole if they are connected by known geometrical relationships, and so on. The connective relationship which unites the parts of an organism into a single *biological* whole is neither merely mechanical or spatial. It is the space-time relationship of directive correlation. A living organism is a 'mechanical' unit, a coherent material body, in the sense that its parts are mechanically connected with one another. But it is a 'biological' unit only in the sense that its parts are connected by directive correlations which have the preservation of the organism as an ultimate focal condition.

The reader who has before his eyes the mathematical definition of directive correlation given in § 20 will ask how the idea of directive correlations which have the self-preservation of the organism as a focal condition may be translated into mathematical terms. How, in other words, can we formally express 'self-preservation' as the focal condition of a directive correlation? 'Self-preservation' is a vague concept and the answer to this question calls for a definition. I think we are expressing most of what we want to express if we say by way of definition that a directive correlation has the *self-preservation* of the organism as a focal condition if the equations (9), § 20 represent necessary and sufficient conditions that the organism should continue to exist throughout some finite span of time in the subsequent natural development of S. The reader may feel that there is a slight difference in meaning between 'preservation' and 'continued existence'. But we are not dealing in this definition with a continued existence that is unconditional: it is assumed to be dependent on necessary conditions and these necessary conditions come to be fulfilled through purpose-like activity. And, surely, that is exactly what is meant by 'preservation'. These observations may be extended to the generalized definition of directive correlation given in § 25.

So far we have only considered those integrating relationships in living organisms in which the directively correlated variables are the sole relata. But the directive correlations which are found in a living organism may themselves stand in certain integrative relationships to one another. For instance, it may be possible for two or more distinct directive correlations to be in turn directively correlated to one another. We then get a relationship of subservience to the whole which, though based on straightforward directive correlations, yet transcends these.

There are different ways in which directive correlations may be related to one another in a typically purposive manner. For instance, we often have an activity going on in an organism whose 'goal' is to create the physiological conditions necessary for the proper functioning of another purposive activity, as when one organ makes it its special business to create the physiological conditions necessary for the proper functioning of another. In other words, a typical case is that in which one set of activities in the organism, directively correlated *inter se*, has as focal condition the creation, maintenance, or regulation of the special physiological conditions which are required by another set of activities directively correlated *inter se*. In homeostasis we have met several representative examples of this form of subservience. From the formal point of view the precise nature of the relationships here involved is the following.

The fundamental idea underlying our precise definition of directive correlation was that of a closed physical system capable of existing in a variety of states each specifiable by the current values of a finite set of physical parameters. Now, as a rule, it will be true that the existence of any directive correlation will depend on certain special conditions being fulfilled not only by the correlated parameters but also by some of the other parameters. For instance, equation (12) is only assumed to be satisfied if the variables $x_1^{t_0}, x_2^{t_0}, ..., x_{k-1}^{t_0}, x_{k+1}^{t_0}, ..., x_n^{t_0}$ possess special values, and in certain cases this may be a necessary condition for the existence of the directive correlation. When restrictions on parameters other than the correlated parameters are necessary conditions for the existence of a directive correlation, we shall speak of the parameters concerned as *parameters of specialization*, and of the special values which a particular directive correlation may require them to have, as the *constants of specialization*. If I kick a ball with one leg it is a necessary condition of this directive correlation that the weight of my body is in the meantime supported by the other leg. Now the maintenance of this condition in turn requires adaptive and coordinated muscular activity and hence directive correlation. We see, therefore, that an important way in which one directive correlation may serve another is for the first to have as focal condition the constancy of one or more of the parameters of specialization of the second.

Another typical manner in which two or more directive correlations A, B,..., may be integrated in the living organism, exists when the focal conditions of A, B,..., are in turn the directively correlated variables of a further and, in this sense, 'higher' directive correlation; in other words, when the 'goal' of one purposive activity is adapted to the 'goal' of another.

To take a familiar example, in many ball games the player when striking or throwing the ball shifts his weight forward in order to impart the maximum thrust to the ball. The arm movements made in striking or throwing the ball involve a set of coordinated activities having a definite focal condition, viz. to speed the ball in a certain direction. The action of shifting the weight of the body is also based on a set of coordinated activities having a definite focal condition, viz. to increase the thrust of the arm. Now in a really integrated movement the action of the body is coordinated with the action of the arms, and both the above focal conditions are therefore in turn directively correlated variables in a higher directive correlation whose focal condition is that the ball shall receive a certain maximum thrust in a certain direction. This focal condition, of course, may in turn be a directively correlated variable in an even higher correlation, as when the direction of this thrust is coordinated with the movements of other players in the field.

In this manner, as in the manner mentioned earlier on, it is possible for directive correlations to form entire hierarchies. In these hierarchies the focal condition of each directive correlation on one level of the hierarchy figures as either a directively correlated variable or a parameter of specialization in the next higher level. Such hierarchic relationships are particularly characteristic of living organisms. They enable us to distinguish, as was done earlier on in this section, between 'proximate' and 'ultimate' focal conditions of a set of directive correlations.

In short, the characteristic unity of the higher living organisms derives from the fact that their activities are united by hierarchies of directive correlations. The biological unity of a living organism is essentially the unity of such an hierarchy, at whose apex we have the focal condition of self-preservation.

§ 34. *The Morphogenetic Field*

In the study of regeneration and of certain stages in the development of embryos the concept of a 'morphogenetic field' has proved valuable and gained widespread currency. Although this field concept has come to acquire a reasonably definite denotation, in the sense that modern biologists are in fair agreement about the phenomena which may be taken to represent such a field, the connotation of the concept is still very indefinite and no satisfactory definition of a 'field' in this sense has been found. For instance, it is often asked what exactly a morphogenetic field is a field *of*, and no satisfactory answer to this question has so far been put forward. In the present section we shall attempt to clarify this 'field' concept.

Being one of the best known cases, the regeneration of the amphibian limb may be taken as a convenient example.

If a limb is removed from one of those amphibia which retain the power of limb-regeneration in the adult or nearly adult stage, i.e. in Urodeles, the regeneration bud formed from the remaining stump manifests all the phenomena generally accepted as characteristic of a morphogenetic field. The stump will grow and differentiate into a new limb, and it will do so even if it is first interfered with in various surgical ways. For instance, it may be first transplanted to another region of the body; or, a part of the stump tissue (e.g. its epidermis or its bone) may be replaced by foreign tissue (e.g. lung tissue or incorrect bone); again, it may have some extra tissue artificially added to it or some of its own tissue removed. In all these cases the stump will eventually give rise to a normal regenerate.

The quantity of limb material which can 'carry the field' is reported to be remarkably small. Even a thin transverse slice of fore-limb for example, if healed onto the stump of a hind limb, will give rise to a fore-limb regenerate.

Great though these powers of regeneration are, they are nevertheless subject to definite limitations. In a certain sense only a whole structure can be regenerated; not individual components. If the skeletal part of a limb is removed the bones are not regenerated, but the gap is filled with connective tissue instead. Another limitation is that imposed by the inherent axiation of the bud. If the stump is turned round and healed into place so that regeneration would have to occur from the originally proximal part of the limb, if at all, only replications of the stump itself occur. If the limb is bisected longitudinally instead of being amputated transversely, no normal cross-section will be regenerated although there may be a certain amount of unorganized growth. On the other hand, a 'split' limb cut transversely across its base will regenerate a normal cross-section. The presence of the peripheral innervation seems to be necessary for the regenerative process, but its action appears to be trophic rather than determinative. All the cells for the regenerate arise from cells of the de-differentiating stump.

These characteristic phenomena of regeneration can now be seen to be another complex manifestation of directive correlation. In effect, the regenerating stump is a region of the body in which the positions taken up by some 'unstable' elements, or the differentiations of the developing tissue, are directively correlated with the positions taken up by other unstable elements or with tissue differentiations in other parts of the region. In short, we have a complex system of coordinated, and so directively correlated, physiological, and morphological processes; the focal conditions of these directive correlations are mutually integrated in the sense discussed in the last section, and the ultimate focal condition of this whole complex or hierarchy of integrated directive correlations consists of the formation of a 'normal' limb.

The fact that the limb bud, and hence the initial condition of the regenerating limb, can be interfered with in a considerable variety of ways without affecting the final regenerate, means no more than that there exists a considerable number of variables in the stump, i.e. in the initial state of the regenerating limb, which are coenetic variables in respect of the directive correlations involved in the coordinated activities of the subsequent process of regeneration. The degree of interference permissible in each case indicates the range of the respective maximum variations (page 90). The independence of the final character of the regenerate from such initial interference thus proves to be of the same type as the independence between the focal condition and the coenetic variables in a directive correlation (§ 14).

The limitations of the regenerative process illustrated above do no more than reflect the 'constants of specialization' of the directive correlations involved.

For instance, the fact that the removal of the skeletal part of the limb stump impedes the regeneration of the bones means that some physical variables connected with the existence of the skeletal parts of the stump are parameters of specialization in the directively correlated activities of bone formation.

The fact that a very thin slice of stump can 'carry the field' may be interpreted to mean that most of the constants of specialization of the essential directive processes involved in the initial stages of limb regeneration are general cell properties and not localized in any particular part of the stump.

We see, therefore, that the field concept refers to the existence within a region of the body of a certain complex system of integrated directive correlations between the variables relating to the structure and morphological development of that region. And the answer to the question what the morphogenetic field is a field *of*, is seen to be the following: in an abstract sense the 'field' is a field of directive correlations. In a more concrete sense it is a field of either coenetic variables, parameters of specialization, directively correlated variables, or integrated focal conditions—according to whether the context is the interference with the initial state of the stump, the limitations of the morphogenetic process, the apparent purposiveness of the constituent events of this process, or their mutual coordination. A critical analysis thus shows that the traditional concept of the 'morphogenetic field' stands for four or five different conceptions, each of which, however, can be made precise when required.

§ 35. *Directive Correlation and Rational Behaviour*

The rational behaviour of man involves a type of adaptive behaviour which requires special consideration. A number of points dealing with this have already been touched briefly in § 15. Here we have a type of activity which is 'purposive' in the full psychological sense of the word. That is to say, we are here dealing with activities involving rational thought processes and proceeding according to a preconceived plan, fixed resolution, and conscious purpose in the mind of the agent. We have mentioned[1] the analogy between purposiveness in this original, subjective, and psychological sense on the one hand, and, on the other, the objective purposive character of actions that are directively correlated to their environment.

The important point is that we must not allow the analogy between these two senses of 'adaptation' to obscure their

[1] § 15.

difference. Whenever there is a danger of confusion we shall refer to the former as 'subjective adaptation' and to the latter as 'objective adaptation'. But unless mention is made to the contrary we shall continue to take the term 'adaptation' by itself to stand for 'objective adaptation' only.

In the subjective sense, 'adaptation' refers to the mental process in which a man decides on the behaviour which in given environmental conditions seems to him most appropriate for achieving a particular goal. The correlation here involved is between the actions he decides upon and the opportunities he believes to exist in his environment. It is a correlation between ideas and decisions in the mind of the agent and as such it lies outside the scope of this book.

'Adaptation' in the objective sense, on the other hand, refers to a correlation between physical variables, viz. the correlation we have come to know as 'directive correlation', and it refers, therefore, to objective, physical system properties. These objective properties can be possessed by any organism irrespective of whether it has the faculty of rational thought or not. There exists, therefore, no necessary connexion between 'subjective' and 'objective' adaptation. Either is possible without the other.

The physical events involved in *successful* rational behaviour are most likely to contain instances of directive correlation in the objective physical sense of our definitions. For if a purposive human action is successful otherwise than accidentally, our preliminary analysis has already shown that the non-accidental character of such success rests on the objective system property of directive correlation, i.e. on the fact that the agent at the time of acting was objectively so conditioned that there exists a finite range of alternative environments, such that if the environment had differed from the actual one in a manner requiring a modified response, the agent would, within certain limits, have carried out the appropriate modification. In such cases of successful activity the event whose occurrence the agent thought of and intended to bring about, i.e. his 'goal', will actually occur, and this actual occurrence is the focal

condition of the directive correlation between his actual behaviour and the actual environment. In this objective conception of the situation rational thought processes may be
said to have been responsible for the achievement of the 'goal'
only in the sense that the corresponding physical brain processes or brain conditions formed a part of, or brought about,
the physical relations which are involved in the directive
correlation.

But it would be wrong to assume that every human action
which springs from the pursuit of a conscious purpose and proceeds according to a preconceived plan, automatically comes
to constitute an instance of behaviour which is directively
correlated to its environment in the objective sense of our
definitions. Unsuccessful and accidentally successful actions
may be truly purposive in the psychological sense, truly adaptive in the subjective sense, and yet in no way directively
correlated to the environment. Nor can we accept the converse
as true, viz. that all human actions which are directively correlated to their environment owe this correlation to the intervention of brain processes or brain conditions which we recognize
as conscious thought processes, and to the presence of conscious purposes and fixed resolutions in the mind of the agent.

We conclude, therefore, that rational thought processes are,
in general, neither necessary nor sufficient conditions for the
occurrence of human behaviour which is directively correlated
to the agent's environment in the precise objective sense of our
definitions.

One result of our analysis was that each instance of directive
correlation presupposes the existence of a certain minimum
number of causal connexions. If an action A is objectively
adapted to some environmental circumstance E in respect of
a given focal condition FC, there must, as we know, exist some
environmental coenetic variable CV, and the minimum number of causal connexions required is shown in the arrow diagram (Fig. 10). It follows that no amount of mental activity,
no faculty of prediction, in Man can bring about an instance of behaviour objectively adapted to the environment,

unless these causal conditions of directive correlation are fulfilled; although, of course, the objective brain processes involved in such mental activity may play an integral part in
bringing them about. In particular, objectively adapted
behaviour requires the causal connexions $CV \rightarrow A$ and
$CV \rightarrow E$. The first is the most interesting one. It is the one
which is normally established by the following chain of causal

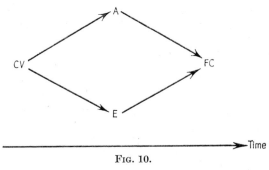

Fig. 10.

connexions: environmental event $\rightarrow$ sense impression $\rightarrow$
afferent nerve impulses $\rightarrow$ central nervous activity $\rightarrow$ efferent
impulses $\rightarrow$ motor activity. The fundamental biological significance of this chain of causal connexions can only be fully
understood in the context of the directive correlations which
it makes possible. In other words, only against the background
of the complete pattern symbolized in Fig. 10 is this chain of
connexion seen in its proper biological perspective. Evidently
the remarks made in § 31 about the fundamental significance
of nerve systems may be extended to sense organs. Giant
molecules, crystals, &c., require sense organs no more than they
require nerve systems. Living organisms, on the other hand,
may require them in so far as the maintenance of their existence
depends on the objective adaptation of their behaviour to the
environment, and hence on patterns of causal connexions of
the type shown in Fig. 10.

The conclusion that the faculty of rational thought in living
organisms can create no exception to these physical requirements of objectively adapted behaviour, forms part of a
general conclusion which will emerge more clearly as our

analysis proceeds, and which has some bearing on an important philosophical question, viz. on the question whether, or in what sense, Man may be called master of his own fate. This conclusion is that, although rational thought is a powerful instrument, it is neither a generally necessary nor sufficient condition for the objective adaptation of Man's behaviour to his environment; for social adjustment and the harmonious integration of the individual into a social unit; for peace and security, or any other objective state of affairs based on directive correlation. For all these things Man depends objectively on the laws which govern the physical property of directive correlation as such and determine its occurrence, growth, or decline in nature. What are these laws? We do not know. As a physical property capable of exact theoretical investigation directive correlation is a newcomer. We have no exact scientific knowledge about the behaviour of this physical property at all. We have only just discovered that it *is* a physical property. But we have no exact knowledge about such questions as whether the growth or decline of the degrees or range of its existence in nature follows exact laws; how extensively it exists outside living nature; whether it can arise spontaneously in a physical system or (as usually appears to be the case) only as the result of other directive correlations, &c. This general conclusion of our analysis, that the destiny of Man depends primarily on relationships of purposiveness in nature which are objective and about which we have no exact scientific information, has considerable philosophical and theological significance. But to enter into the discussion of such wider questions would take us beyond the scope of this work.

§ 36. *The Nature of Instinctive Behaviour*

The problem of the 'instincts' so-called, has been a perennial problem in the discussion of animal behaviour. As mere phenomena instincts are, of course, well known and there is no significant disagreement among biologists about their peculiarities. But when it comes to interpreting their theoretical significance the picture changes. The provocative purposiveness of many instinctive behaviour patterns, such as in the social instincts of insects or the nesting and migratory habits of birds, together with the vagueness of the concepts biologists have used in interpreting these phenomena, make it hardly surprising that throughout the centuries the subject has occupied such a controversial position in philosophy, biology, and theology. The terms 'instinct' or 'instinctive' evidently stand in the same urgent need of explication as the other concepts relating to the apparent purposiveness of organic activities, and it will be worth while indicating briefly how the concept of directive correlation may help us in this respect. It will be sufficient to confine ourselves to the concept of instinctive behaviour and to see what precise meaning can be given to it.

In the ninth edition of the *Encyclopaedia Britannica* 'instinctive behaviour' was defined by G. J. Romanes as 'the conscious performance of actions that are adaptive in character but pursued without necessary knowledge of the relation between the means employed and the ends attained'.[1] In later editions this definition was supplemented by Lloyd Morgan's description:

instinctive behaviour comprises those complex groups of co-ordinated acts which, though they contribute to experience, are on their first occurrence not determined by individual experience; which are adaptive and tend to the well-being of the individual and the preservation of the race; which are due to the co-operation of external and internal stimuli; which are similarly performed by all members of the same more or less restrictive group of animals; but which are subject to variation and to subsequent modifications under the guidance of individual experience.

We may accept these passages as a sufficient guide to the contemporary meaning of the term 'instinctive'. But before we can attempt to make this meaning precise in terms of directive correlation, one or two observations are necessary on the meaning of 'behaviour'. It is generally agreed that

---

[1] This definition may be compared with that given in the dictionary of philosophy and psychology: 'an inherited reaction of the sensory-motor type relatively complex and markedly adaptive in character and common to a group of individuals'. A similar definition is given in the *Oxford English Dictionary*.

'behaviour' in biological contexts refers to the external activities or reactions of an organism as distinct from its internal activities. But the concept would obviously become too wide if it were taken to cover the totality of external activities or reactions at any particular point of time. It will be more in keeping with biological usage if we restrict the term to *coordinated* activities. But even this seems to be too wide a concept and requires a further qualification. It is obviously desirable to exclude from 'behaviour'[1] the slow, coordinated, morphological changes which may accompany the growth and ontogenetic development of an individual. Hence coordination must here be restricted to 'short-term' coordination, that is to say, coordination in which the directively correlated variables and the coenetic variables are separated by a short-time interval only (§ 30).

The most important point to note about instinctive behaviour is that its purposive character derives from two sources, from two kinds of adaptation. In the first place from what was described in § 30 as *immediate adaptation* and, secondly from *phylogenetic adaptation*. We are therefore concerned with short-term and long-term directive correlations and, as in all cases which comprise mixed forms of directive correlation, we must be careful to distinguish these.

Let us begin with the immediate adaptations. Every pattern of instinctive behaviour involves short-term directive correlation not only because it involves coordinated activities but also because these activities are to some degree adapted to current environmental conditions. For instance, when a bird builds a nest this involves a complex set of coordinated activities which must be capable of immediate adaptation to special environmental conditions. The flights of the bird must be adapted to the distribution of suitable constructional material in its neighbourhood, to the obstacles that appear in its path, to the position of the nest and so on. Even in such simple cases as when a young caterpillar instinctively crawls towards a light source, its movements involve both coordination and

---

[1] *Animal* behaviour, at any rate.

simple immediate adaptations to particular environmental conditions, such as to the particular nature of the ground over which it moves.

Now the characteristic property of instinctive behaviour is that these immediate adaptations, and the apparent purposiveness which the behaviour derives from them, are not brought about by rational thought processes. Nor are they in the first instance acquired by learning or, speaking generally, by experience. They are, in fact, *innate* characteristics of the organism. If it had not been for our analysis of directive correlation this statement might appear obscure. How, it might be asked, can the apparent purposiveness of behaviour be an innate characteristic? But there is no real obscurity here. Our analysis has shown that directive correlation is a physical system-property and there is no reason why, as a physical property, it should not be an innate one. The fact that the caterpillar in a purpose-like manner adapts its crawling movements to the nature of the ground, involves a short-term directive correlation in which the approach of the caterpillar to the light figures as a focal condition. This directive correlation is a physical property of the caterpillar + environment system, which presupposes that the caterpillar has certain specific physical properties. And there is no reason why these properties should not be an innate characteristic of the caterpillar. Now the important point is that the possession of this innate characteristic may be a phylogenetic adaptation to the environment, and this, no doubt, is always implied if we speak of 'instinctive' behaviour. In that case the caterpillar's behaviour will derive from this fact a purposive character which is additional to that already derived from the immediate adaptations which it involves.

Instinctive behaviour may therefore be defined as behaviour whose constituent activities stand in short-term directive correlations to the environment, but which as a whole, i.e. as a coherent set of correlated activities united by a single focal condition, may be regarded as a single variable whose value is phylogenetically adapted to the environment.

The element of purposiveness derived from the short-term directive correlations and that derived from its phylogenetic adaptation, i.e. from long-term directive correlations, may be present in instinctive behaviour in widely varying proportions. In those cases of instinctive behaviour in which the latter particularly outshines the former we speak of particularly 'blind' instincts. For instance, when a hen hatches its eggs the degree of immediate adaptation of the action is comparatively small. Its behaviour will be adapted to the position of the nest and the position of the eggs in the nest. But if an egg is placed outside the nest the bird will not retrieve it. This particular hypothetical variation of the egg's position lies therefore already outside the 'maximum variation' of the short-term directive correlations of the hatching behaviour; and in this respect short-term directive correlations are dwarfed by the high degree of phylogenetic adaptation involved in the breeding habits of birds. The hatching instinct of the bird therefore appears to us as a comparatively 'blind' instinct. Another typical example in which the long-term directive correlations greatly outshine the short-term directive correlations is *Rhynchites betulae* (§ 4). Here we have again a very high degree of phylogenetic adaptation combined with a comparatively low degree of immediate adaptation. Contrasting examples are largely restricted to higher organisms. The outstanding case in which the immediate adaptations often outshine the phylogenetic adaptations is, of course, the behaviour of Man.

Although primarily based on innate characteristics, instinctive behaviour may undergo adaptive modifications in the course of the life-history of the individual and may come to be modified in the light of his current experiences. In other words, instinctive patterns of behaviour other than those occurring for the first time in the life of the individual may also involve ontogenetic adaptations. A special case of this is when experience results in a widening of the maximum variation, and hence of the degree, of the immediate adaptations involved in the behaviour. For instance, bees and ants gradually learn to find their way home to the nest from ever more remote regions

of the environment owing to increased topographical knowledge acquired in earlier explorations. Instincts which are not
susceptible to ontogenetic adaptations are known as 'rigid'
instincts. But ontogenetic adaptations of this kind are excluded
from the concept of instinct as such. We say of such modified
behaviour patterns that they are partly based on instinct
and partly on experience. The fact remains, therefore, that
behaviour is 'instinctive' only in so far as it involves sets of
short-term directive correlations based on phylogenetic adaptations, i.e. based on long-term directive correlations.

A notable result of our analysis is that it shows instinctive
behaviour to involve no new principle beyond the principle of
directive correlation. The problem of instinctive behaviour is
thus seen to be no more than a particular aspect of the general
problem of directive correlation in life processes. That is to
say, by and large the significance, origin, working, and inheritance of patterns of instinctive behaviour in nature are neither
more nor less mysterious than the significance, origin, working, and inheritance of other forms of directive correlation such
as are found in homeostasis or morphogenesis. Admittedly,
there is a difference between the type of directive correlation
which may exist between the actions of different members of
an animal society, as in the social insects, and the form which
exists between the activities of different parts of a single
organism, as in homeostasis: in the former case there may be
no permanent mechanical connexion between the individuals,
whereas in the latter case the organs are mechanically connected. This, however, is not so much a difference in the actual
relationship of directive correlation as in the particular facili-
ties which are available for the causal connexions which the
respective directive correlations require. These differences will
be discussed in a later section.

§ 37. *The Nature of Learning*

In the preceding section 'instinctive behaviour' was defined
as behaviour whose constituent activities stand in short-term
directive correlations to the environment but which as a whole,

i.e. as a coherent set of activities united by a single focal condition, may be regarded as a variable whose value is phylogenetically adapted to the environment. In this respect it is instructive to contrast instinctive behaviour with *learnt* behaviour. In learnt behaviour we also have a set of activities standing in short-term directive correlations to the environment, but in this case the distinctive feature of this set as a whole is not that it is a phylogenetic adaptation to the environment but an *ontogenetic* adaptation. In learning the animal makes systemic adjustments which in general take long to effect as compared with its normal reaction time and which are part of the gradual ontogenetic adjustment of the individual to the special demands made upon him by the environment. Whereas, therefore, the outstanding characteristic of instinctive behaviour is that it is a combination of short-term and long-term directive correlations, learnt behaviour is a combination of short-term and medium-term directive correlations. Although the example of ontogenetic adaptation given in § 29 was already an example of learnt behaviour, another illustration may be given here of the manner in which the spatio-temporal relations involved in learning may be analysed with precision.

Consider a rat learning to run a maze, and assume that if a certain training method is adopted the animal requires three weeks to learn to run the maze without error. Let us illustrate the medium-term directive correlations which exist in this case.

In learning the maze the behaviour pattern of the rat becomes adapted to the plan, the layout, of the maze. In this case of adaptation the plan of the maze is regarded as a variable: the concept implies the possibility of a maze having been chosen with an alternative layout. And the main implication of the idea of adaptation here is that there exists a range of possible alternative mazes which are such that at the end of three weeks of training (but no sooner) the rat is able to run without error whichever one of them has been used throughout that training period (but no other). How large this ensemble of possible alternative mazes for any particular type of rat is, only experiment can tell. But common sense would suggest that it includes, for instance, all mazes which compel the rat to select the correct turning from a choice of two or three alternatives at as many points along the correct route as does the maze actually used.

To exemplify how the medium-term directive correlations prevailing in that case may be given a precise formulation, let us proceed as follows. Assume that there are n points along the correct route at which the rat is confronted with a choice between two or three alternative paths, only one being correct. For each of these n points let us introduce a variable X_i, where i designates the point in question; and let X_i by definition have the value 1, 2, or 3, according to whether the correct choice at the ith point is to turn left, to go straight, or to turn right. The values of the variables $X_1, X_2, ..., X_n$ are therefore the 'key' to the maze; let the key to the maze actually used be $X'_1, X'_2, ..., X'_n$. Next let us introduce a set of variables $Y_1, Y_2, ..., Y_n$, each of which refers to the point of the maze indicated by its suffix and has by definition the value 1, 2, or 3, according to whether the animal in any given attempt to run the maze turns left, goes straight, or turns right when it reaches the respective point of the maze; each variable has the value 0 if the animal does none of these things or fails to reach the respective point. A run without error through the maze actually used is therefore characterized by $X'_i = Y'_i$, for $i = 1, 2, ..., n$. Since we are assuming that the same maze is used throughout the three weeks of training, the process of learning the maze here refers to a conception of the rat-plus-maze system in which the values of $X_1, X_2, ..., X_n$ are constant in time, i.e. $X_i^{t_1} = X_i^{t_0}$.

At the end of the three weeks the rat has learnt to run the maze without error and every time it does so it performs a set of activities of which the following is true. In the first place, the activities are coordinated and involve immediate adaptations to the environment. For while the rat is completing any particular stretch of the maze its movements are adapted to the nature of the ground over which it runs, the obstacles in its path, &c. These are short-term directive correlations between its locomotion and the environment of the general type discussed in § 27.

Secondly, the sequence of choices made by the rat at the n turning-points or cross-roads is adapted to the plan of the maze in a medium-term directive correlation. In precise terms: if at the end of the training period, say at t_1, the rat runs the maze without error, the set of values $Y_1^{t_1}, Y_2^{t_1}, ..., Y_n^{t_1}$ is directively correlated[1] to the set of values $X_1^{t_1}, X_2^{t_1}, ..., X_n^{t_1}$. The coenetic variable of this directive correlation is the set of values $X_1^{t_0}, X_2^{t_0}, ..., X_n^{t_0}$, where t_0 denotes the beginning of the training period. For ex hypothesi we are dealing only with mazes for which the rat requires exactly three weeks of training, and the coenetic variable is therefore the choice of maze made at the beginning of that training period. The directive correlation is thus seen to be of the medium-term type, the directively correlated variables being separated from the coenetic variable by at least three weeks. The focal condition of this directive correlation is that the rat should successfully complete the course through the maze.

We may, of course, regard not only the whole sequence of choices made by the rat in any one successful run as adapted to the plan of the maze but also any one individual choice. In the latter conception we are envisaging a narrower ensemble, viz. one in which the alternative mazes differ in a Y-value at the respective individual turning-point only.

§ 38. Biological Memory

In the philosophy of biology particular emphasis has often been given to the characteristic power of living organisms to bring the past to bear upon the present. This general phenomenon is often called 'biological memory', and the conscious memory-function of Man is regarded as its highest manifesta-

---

[1] Sets of variables may be said to be directively correlated in the same sense as single variables; for a set of variables may be regarded as a single variable each of whose values corresponds to a particular constellation of the values of the members of the set.

tion. Frequently this power is held up as one of the most outstanding features of life, and sometimes also as a criterion of biological progress. Man, it has been said, differs from all other forms of life in the immensely greater power he has to bring to bear upon any instance of his present behaviour not only his own past experience but also, through the spoken or written word, that of the entire race.

What is the nature of this power? If taken literally, the assertion that living organisms can bring the past to bear upon the present merely affirms the principle of causality. Inasmuch as *any* deterministic physical event may be represented as a causal function of prior physical events it may be taken to be just another instance in which the past has come to bear upon the present. But in the biological context a good deal more is meant than just this, and the causal relations which biologists denote by 'biological memory' have a number of special, and sometimes perplexing, characteristics. Of these the most important would seem to be the following:

(i) The organism's reactions to an external stimulus appear to be influenced not only by immediately preceding events but also by events which occurred in the comparatively remote past. This influence often gives the impression of being a peculiarly direct and obvious one. The causal connexions concerned, therefore, are conceived to bridge a more or less extensive time interval and at least three points of time are involved: the time of the reaction, the immediately preceding time of the external stimulus, and the rather more remote past at which one of the experiences occurred which influence the organism's present reaction to the given stimulus. We may denote these points of time by t_3, t_2, and t_1 respectively.

(ii) We know that this influence of past experience on its present behaviour does not as a rule occur through the persistence in the organism of after-effects which are narrowly localized and constant in time, that is to say, through what is commonly visualized as persistent 'traces' or 'engrams'. In other words, the influence of the remote past on the present does not as a rule occur in a manner analogous to that in which gramophone records, photographs, books, &c., can carry the past into the present and bridge large intervals of time. Hence, on the face of it, it is difficult to see what form these causal connexions take and the impression given by biological memory is often that of a time interval being 'jumped' rather than 'bridged'.

(iii) Biological memory does not mean that living organisms merely have power to bring the past to bear upon the present gratuitously, but, rather, in a goal-directed and purposive way.

Let us try to clarify these three peculiarities and, in particular, to examine their compatibility with the conceptual framework of a deterministic physics.

The first creates no essential difficulty from the physical point of view. To say that the reaction R of the organism at the time t_3 to the stimulus S at t_2 is influenced by some event E which occurred at some remotely antecedent point of time t_1 means that, in a representation of the organism and the relevant part of its environment as a single closed system, the prevailing system properties are such that, given the system with t_1 as initial time and the stimulus S at t_2 as part of the system, a hypothetical variation of E at t_1 would have entailed a variation of R at t_3. In other words, R_{t_3} is a causal function of E_{t_1}, and we have here a perfectly ordinary causal connexion as defined in § 18. The length of the interval between t_1 and t_3 is irrelevant to the validity of this conception and the fact that E_{t_1} may precede R_{t_3} by a long interval, perhaps a matter of years, does not therefore raise any epistemological difficulties.

Nor is there any essential difficulty, or incompatibility with the concepts of physics, in the second peculiarity of biological memory, viz. that a living organism appears to be capable of letting past events influence present behaviour by means other than physiological traces which are strictly localized within the organism and comparatively constant in time. However, this is not an altogether easy point and confusions on it are widespread. If an organism brings a past event to

bear upon its present behaviour this past event must, of
course, have left after-effects in (or outside) the organism.
That is merely a tautology. But the point is that these after
effects need not, as some biologists have rashly assumed, take
the form of 'engrams' in the above sense. They need not be in
any visualizable form of 'stored information'.

Suppose we have a physical system in which the values at
a time t_3 of a certain set A of state-parameters are causal
functions of the t_1-values of another set C of parameters,
where t_1 precedes t_3 by a comparatively large time interval.
Next, suppose that t_2 is any intermediate point of time and
that B_{t_2} is the set of all those t_2-values of the system's state-
parameters of which one or more members of the set A_{t_3} are
causal functions and which in turn are causal functions of one
or more members of the set C_{t_1}. We can accordingly write

$$A_{t_3} = \phi(B_{t_2}) = \eta(C_{t_1})$$

and
$$B_{t_2} = \zeta(C_{t_1}).$$

Finally, assume that η is a simple and determinable function
whereas ϕ and ζ are complicated and undeterminable, and
that not only the values of the members of B_{t_2} depend on the
time chosen as t_2 but also the very membership of B_{t_2}, i.e. the
identity of the variables it comprises.

Now, if A_{t_3} is interpreted to stand for some action of the
organism at the time t_3 while C_{t_1} is interpreted to stand for
some experience the organism had at t_1, the above assumptions
in their simple way create exactly the typical state of affairs
we have in biological memory.

In the first place, the fact that η is a simple determinable
function whereas ϕ and ζ are not, will tend to give the impression that the A_{t_3} is determined by the remote experience C_{t_1}
in that apparently direct manner which is often such a notice-
able feature of biological memory. In the second place, the
above assumptions show A_{t_3} to be a causal function of C_{t_1}
although nothing of the nature of a localized and constant
'trace' or 'engram' of C_{t_1} persists throughout the interval t_1

to t_3. For the assumption that both the membership of B_{t_2} and the values of its members vary with t_2 implies that the after-effects of C_{t_1} are neither strictly localized within the organism nor constant in time. Hence, these after-effects cannot be of the kind commonly visualized as 'trace' or 'engram'.

This simplified model, therefore, shows how in a manner perfectly consistent with deterministic physics the present activities of an organism can stand in some obvious or simple relation to an experience which it had some time ago, without standing in an obvious or simple relation to any of the intermediate states through which the organism passed since that experience; it shows how the remote past can come to enter into the causal determination of the organism's present behaviour without the intervention of 'traces' or 'engrams', in the traditional sense of these terms.

Finally, we come to the third implication of biological memory, viz. that the causal connexions which biological memory establishes between past events and present organic behaviour, play an integral part in the purposive quality of such behaviour. This implication gives us the clue to the main biological significance of these causal connexions and to the most fundamental function of biological memory in the phenomena of life. For we know directive correlation to be the objective basis of this end-serving and purpose-like quality and we know that each instance of directive correlation presupposes a certain number of causal connexions. These causal connexions may be divided into two classes: those which link the coenetic variables with the directively correlated variables, and those which link the latter with the focal conditions. Of these two classes it is obviously the first which is supplied by biological memory. The causal connexions to which the concept of biological memory in the usual biological context refers, are in fact little else than the causal connexions between coenetic variables and directively correlated variables required by the directive correlation of life processes to one another and to the environment.

Biological memory, i.e. the power of living organisms in

some purposive manner to bring the comparatively remote pasts to bear upon their present behaviour, is thus seen to be merely a certain aspect of the general phenomena of directive correlation. It involves no new principles, and all those of its peculiarities which were considered in this section are compatible with the ordinary assumptions of physical determinism.

V

THE GENERAL NATURE OF LIFE

§ 39. *The Difference Between Living and Non-Living*
Systems

THE form and structure of any solid and elastic body enjoys a
certain independence from contingent environmental disturbances. Its solidity causes the body to resist mechanical deformation and its elasticity causes it to resume its normal
form after the deforming forces have ceased to act, provided
the latter do not exceed specific limits. The power of a material
body to resist deformation and to restore its normal shape or
structure may be denoted as *mechanical stability*. In the case
of any mechanically stable body, therefore, there exists a
range of possible external forces of which it can be said that
they would permanently alter the body's shape or architec-
ture were it not for this physical property of mechanical
stability. The degree of this power is given by the magnitude
of the range of possible external forces against which the body's
mechanical stability renders it immune. Solids, in the everyday sense, are not the only mechanically stable bodies. Gels,
membranes, films, fibres, and other structures of which living
organisms are composed possess varying degrees of mechanical
stability.

In so far as they have a mechanically stable structure, living
organisms share with inorganic bodies a considerable independence from contingent environmental disturbances. Living
organisms are, however, distinguished from inorganic and
dead objects by the fact that their existence derives an additional independence of environmental disturbances from their
power to adapt and adjust their active and passive states
to the environment, to regulate their internal and external
environment, to heal their injuries, to maintain themselves
as going concerns by adaptive, coordinated, or regulated
activities—in short, from their power directively to correlate

M

their active or passive states to one another and to the environment in a way which has the continued existence of the organism as ultimate focal condition. That is to say, in addition to the range of possible environmental disturbances against whose permanent effects a living organism is safeguarded by the mechanical stability of its body, there exists a further range of possible environmental disturbances against whose permanent effects the organism is safe-guarded by the existence of a system of integrated directive correlations which have the continued existence of the organism as an ultimate focal condition: viz. the range of all those possible external disturbances which lie within the 'maximum variation' of these directive correlations. This integrated system of directive correlations is, as we have seen, the essential physical property which makes the organism a biological unit. The property of 'being alive' is therefore essentially the physical property of existing in a manner which enjoys this special type of independence from the environment; *death* is the loss of this property and means the breakdown of the system of directive correlations on which it is based (cf. § 33).

We saw in § 23 that the manner in which the mechanical stability of its body renders the organism independent of certain environmental disturbances is analogous to the manner in which directive correlation confers such independence, except that in the former case we have a correlation between epistemically *dependent* physical variables whereas in the latter the correlated variables are epistemically *independent*.

These two forms of independence from the environment are not isolated from each other. We have already seen that the existence of any directive correlation requires a certain minimum number of causal connexions and that the body makes special provisions for some of these causal connexions by means of nerves and other transmissive machinery. The permanency of all this special transmissive machinery is very largely based on the mechanical stability of the structures involved. We have here an example of how mechanical stability may be used by the body to support the directive correlations of its life processes. Conversely, some of these directively correlated life processes have as a proximate focal condition the safeguarding of the body's transmissive machinery, i.e. the safeguarding of its life-lines. Directive correlation and mechanical stability are thus seen mutually to supplement each other in the living organism in many interlocked and concerted ways.

The advantages which mechanically stable channels can offer for the transmission of both afferent and efferent stimuli may be regarded as one of the reasons why living organisms exist in the form of mechanically connected structures. But this mechanical connexion and transmissive machinery is not a necessary requirement. As we shall see in the following section, an association of animals may be an organized and integrated biological unit in the same sense as a living organism, that is to say, it may be a whole whose parts are related by a system of directive correlations which have the continued existence of the whole as an ultimate focal condition. Yet, in most animal associations the members are individually free and mobile and not connected with one another by permanent mechanical connexions and transmissive machinery. A single organism is both a mechanical unit and a biological unit. An association of animals may be a biological unit without being a mechanical unit. In a certain sense it is therefore comparatively more dependent for its existence on directive correlation than on mechanical stability.

In this connexion it is interesting to note that a physical system which depends for its continued existence entirely on directive correlation and not at all on any form of mechanical stability, not even for the continued existence of its parts, would be perfectly consistent with our definitions and hence also with physical determinism. It would be a physical system without mechanically stable and solid parts; i.e. it would be just a system of physical variables, as intangible and abstract as, say, an electrical field or a shadow. This combination of intangibility with purpose-like behaviour would give it essentially the character of a free or unembodied spirit.

§ 40. *Integrated Social Units*

A living organism is a *mechanical* unit by virtue of the stable mechanical connexions which join its parts to form a single compact body; it is a *biological* unit by virtue of the system of integrated directive correlations which connect the state of each part with that of other parts and which have the continued existence of the organism as an ultimate focal condition. Since we have shown directive correlation to be a *physical* relationship the concept of 'biological unit' in this sense is just as genuine and mathematically definable a physical concept as that of 'mechanical unit', the only difference being that it is based on a different type of physical relationship.

An association of living organisms may or may not be a mechanical unit in the above sense. Its individual members may be mechanically attached to one another as in colonial hydrozoa, or spatially separate and individually mobile as in Man. Now we have seen that directive correlation can exist between the activities or states of different individuals even if there are no permanent mechanical connexions between them, provided that their mutual relation in space and time somehow enables the required causal connexions to come about. These connexions may be established, for instance, through visual, auditory, or tactile signals. It follows that an association of living organisms may be a biological unit in exactly the same sense as a living organism, irrespective of whether it is a mechanical unit or not, viz. when there exists a system of integrated directive correlations which relates the state of each individual member with the state of other members of the association and which has the continued existence of the association as an ultimate focal condition.

We shall call an association of living organisms which is a biological unit in this sense an *integrated social unit* or *society*. Some authors have used such terms as 'social organism' or 'epiorganism' to designate a unit of this kind. Their terminology was no doubt inspired by the fact that in defining these social units they had to fall back on the analogy which exists between the purposive interdependence of the parts of an organism and the purposive interdependence of the members of a society. But this is only a limited analogy and it has often proved to be a misleading one. For instance, it is apt to veil the fact that a society is composed of *individuals*, and this has at times made the concept of a 'social organism' a convenient tool in the hands of political ideologists wishing to minimize the rights of the individual. Since the concept of directive correlation permits an independent definition of integrated social units, it is no longer necessary to invite misunderstandings by speaking of such units as 'organisms'.

Our definition of an integrated social unit as an association of living organisms which are connected by a system of integrated directive correlations having the continued existence of the association as an ultimate focal condition, requires further clarification in three important respects. And in each respect it requires a definite decision if it is to be used without ambiguity. Since, however, different scientific contexts may require different decisions in this respect I shall merely outline the alternatives which lie before us.

In the first place we must decide what is to be meant by the 'continued existence of the association'. Is this to mean the continued existence of the particular individuals of which the association is composed at any particular time, or merely the continued existence of their organization and of their pattern of social relationships? Usually we mean the latter. For instance, when we speak of the continued existence of a business organization or political party. Either interpretation can be given a precise definition, but the second interpretation can obviously be applied only to associations which comprise so large a number of members that the temporary loss of one or more members does not significantly alter the pattern of its organization and social relationships. A pair of friends, for instance, can be regarded as an integrated social unit only in the first sense.

In the second place we must decide whether the directive correlations mentioned in the definition are to include *all* the main types distinguished in § 30, i.e. 'long-', 'medium-', and 'short-term' correlations; or whether the mere existence of one or two of these types should be deemed sufficient to make the association an instance of an 'integrated social unit'. In most animal associations all three types of directive correlation combine to unite the association into an integrated social unit. In a bee colony, for instance, we have many cases of coordinated activity, collaboration, and concerted action which are based on short-term directive correlations between the activities of the individual bees. In addition, we have several kinds of ontogenetic adaptation. Thus, when there is a shortage of nurses, the nursing stage through which each bee passes becomes extended. Finally, there are the very extensive phylogenetic adaptations of the individuals which the social integration of the hive requires.

But suppose that in some animal association there exist mutual adaptations between the members in respect of only one or two of the three main types of adaptation which we have distinguished. The question mainly concerns phylogenetic adaptation: shall an association of living organisms be called an integrated social unit whose members are adapted to one another for their mutual benefit only as far as concerns their phylogenetic adaptation? If we decide that it shall, the concept becomes very wide, for most symbiotic associations would then qualify as integrated social units. Zoophilous flowers and the insects which secure their cross-fertilization, for instance, would then together form 'integrated social units'. It is easy to see that for many scientific purposes a narrower definition would be preferable.

The question also concerns ontogenetic adaptation. Certain colonial forms of life such as colonial coelenterates, *Obelia*, and coral polyps, are associations in which there are phylogenetic and ontogenetic adaptations between the members, but no short-term directive correlations worthy of note. Colonies of this type raise other problems as well and we shall return to them later on. All I am concerned to say at the moment is that the question whether such associations are covered by the term 'integrated social unit' depends on whether or not we demand that the directive correlation mentioned in our definition of that term shall include short- as well as medium- and long-term directive correlations.

In deciding whether an association of living organisms does or does not constitute an integrated social unit on any of these interpretations, it is important to realize the many factors which may have to be taken into account. In some cases this is not at all easy. Although the following two examples are not of integrated social units, they will throw some light on several points arising in this connexion.

The first case is that of a policeman guarding a prisoner. Assume that at a given point of time both are quietly sitting on a bench. Although mentally alert, both are physically inactive. Is the state of the policeman at that moment directively correlated to the state of the prisoner, in the objective, physical sense of our definitions? The answer is Yes: if the policeman is alert, his state is directively correlated to that of the prisoner in a short-term correlation whose focal condition is the prevention of an escape. Because, in the first place, during the episode considered we may presume it to be a necessary and sufficient condition for the prevention of an escape that as long as the prisoner remains on the spot the policeman should do the same. Secondly, there exists a range of conceivable variations of the prisoner's behaviour, viz. attempts to escape, which would require certain counter measures on the part of the policeman. And, thirdly, the policeman *ex hypothesi* is objectively so conditioned that in any such case he would respond with the appropriate counter measure to prevent an escape. All the essential conditions of directive correlation are therefore fulfilled. The question whether in actual fact the prisoner *could* make a successful dash for it, is irrelevant. The point is that there exists a number of conceivable attempts to escape which the policeman *would* frustrate by appropriate reactions. There may exist, of course, conceivable modes of escape which he would be unable to hinder. But that is not the point. The existence of these cases merely shows up the limits of the admissible range of coenetic variation of the prisoner's behaviour, i.e. of the maximum variation of the directive correlation between the policeman and the prisoner.

Next, take the case in which a policeman guards a house against possible burglars and consider an interval of time during which no burglars appear on the scene. What type of objective adaptation is involved in this activity? While he is guarding the house, is the policeman's state directively correlated to all the potential burglars in the district? No, certainly not; no more so in fact than the line of fire of our anti-aircraft gun could be said to be adapted to the target before the latter has come into sight or has been picked up by the radar beam. Yet, guarding a house is certainly an adaptive activity which has the prevention of a burglary as a focal condition.[1] To get an idea of the type of directive correlation which characterizes the activity of guarding an object against some *eventuality*, let us introduce two variables, x and y. The variable x refers to the house and has by definition the value 1 when the house is being burgled and the value 2 when it is not; y refers to the policeman and has the value 1 when he stays on his post and the value 2 when he leaves it. Subject to what conditions can the values of x and y at any particular point of time t_1 be said to be directively correlated in respect of the prevention of a burglary? The answer is, if the circumstances are such that (a) burglary will be prevented if and only if either $x_t = 1$ and $y_t = 1$ or $x_t = 2$ and $y_t = 2$, and (b) there exists a coenetic variable whose actual value and hypothetically considered alternative value have these two cases as respective effects. The main implications of these conditions are, that only such possible burglaries are considered as are detectable and preventable by the policeman; that the latter is objectively so conditioned that he will only leave his post in order to catch a burglar; and that he would actually invite

---

[1] I am not, of course, here concerned with the incidental adaptations which the activity of guarding may involve; e.g. the adaptation involved in keeping one's eyes trained on the house.

a burglary if he left it for other reasons. The coenetic variable of this directive correlation obviously is x_{t_0}, where t_0 may be any point of time preceding t_1 which is such that detection of the crime at t_0 will by t_1 have resulted in appropriate but not as yet effective counter measures on the part of the policeman.

An interesting question is, what exactly the variable x here stands for, restricted as it is by definition to two alternative values only: the house being invaded—house not being invaded. I think the answer is the following. A variable restricted by definition to the two values: 'A occurs' and 'A does not occur' may be interpreted to represent the *possibility* of A occurring. Our example shows, therefore, that under certain circumstances and in the full physical sense of our definitions, the activity of an organism may be said to be objectively adapted to the *possibility* of a certain event occurring in its environment. Similarly, whereas the line of fire of the anti-aircraft gun is adapted only to the actual path of the target, its design may be said to be objectively adapted to the mere possibility of a target appearing within its range.

The upshot of these two illustrations is, first, that even short-term directive correlations can exist between two individuals who are completely inactive at the time; secondly, that it can exist between the behaviour of an individual and the mere *possibility* of a certain state of affairs occurring in his environment. We have also learnt that directive correlations, however obvious they may seem at first sight, upon further analysis may be found to require special assumptions. In the preceding case such necessary assumptions were, for instance, that the policeman would only desert his post in pursuit of a burglar, and that only detectable and preventable burglaries were being considered.

It is important to realize these facts before one sets out to find the directive correlations which may unite living organisms into integrated social units. Thus the points we have just made are relevant in answering the question to what extent such units as human families or pairs of friends may be regarded as integrated social units in the objective sense of our definition.

The fact that the state of one individual can be directively correlated to the mere possibility of certain adverse events happening to another individual shows that in deciding these questions we may not only have to take into account the actual collaboration and division of labour between the members of the unit, but also the 'solidarity' existing between them.

It remains to take up the third respect in which our original definition of integrated social units must be clarified. This concerns the exact meaning of the term 'individual'. Earlier on I have given a definition of a 'biological unit', but since that definition was given in terms of directive correlation and since directive correlations can exist in different degrees, the individuality of a biological unit also becomes a matter of degree, viz. the degree of independence in respect of environmental disturbances which the organism derives from those directive correlations between its state and the state of the environment that have its continued existence as an ultimate focal condition. In some colonial forms of life this degree may be comparatively small and, as in all matters of degree, we are sooner or later up against the question of where to draw the line.

There is no doubt about what is meant by 'an individual' in human society. But it is no easy matter to decide whether we can still speak of 'individuals' in such forms of life as the colonial ascidian *Pyrosoma*, or a colonial hydrozoon such as the Portuguese man-of-war. The latter consists of a float with a sail-like crest from which a number of polyps hang down into the water. Some of these polyps have a nutritive function, others are tactile; some contain batteries of stinging cells, others are male reproductive, and still others give rise to egg-producing medusae. The whole is such that the term 'compound-organism' seems a far better description than 'colony'. As Woodger[1] has pointed out, the main reason why the working biologist regards the members of such a compound organism as individuals is that they are, in a certain technical sense, in

---

[1] 'On Biological Transformations', in *Essays on Growth and Form*, Oxford, 1945.

morphological correspondence with certain single forms of life, in this case with single polyps. This criterion has obvious advantages in taxonomy, although it suffers from the same difficulty as our own criterion in that it also makes individuality a matter of degree. In a general theoretical and philosophical context, however, our definition of a biological 'individual' would seem to be the more appropriate one, since it is based on the most distinctive characteristics of life as such, viz. directive correlation.

This section may be concluded with a few wider considerations. Our analysis has shown that organic integration may in principle be defined in terms of mathematical relations between quantitative variables. Organic integration, and in particular social integration, may therefore be regarded as a *physical* property of material systems. This result has, I believe, fundamental consequences for psychology and theology. Although these consequences cannot be given a full discussion within the framework of this book, one or two theological consequences will be indicated in §§ 42 and 43. A fundamental consequence for psychology would seem to be the following. If the organic integration between the individual and his social environment is a *physical* property of the individual-plus-environment system, it becomes easy to imagine a purely biological basis for the existence in each human individual of an instinctive, largely inarticulate, awareness of the actual degree of integration existing at any time between himself and his social environment, and of an instinctive tendency to react to this experience in characteristic ways. The hypothesis that Man possesses powerful 'security instincts' of this kind appears to me to be a very fruitful one for explaining a number of psychological phenomena (including some religious and sexual ones) which psychologists have hitherto been unable to explain satisfactorily.

§ 41. *The Mechanical Stability of Biological Structures*

So far as our immediate perceptions are concerned, a living organism is a solid body which derives a characteristic independence of environmental disturbances partly from its solidity and partly from purposive activity. This is the basic phenomenon of life. Our analysis has given this phenomenon a precise formulation in terms of mechanical stability and directive correlation. Of these two sources of independence one—directive correlation—has been discussed at length in the preceding chapters. The other—mechanical stability—has so far received only little attention in our work. One reason for this disproportionate emphasis is that directive correlation supplies the most truly distinctive characteristics of life whereas mechanical stability does not; another reason is that in the exposure and analysis of the former this book attempts to break fresh ground, whereas the nature of mechanical stability is a thoroughly explored physical question to which the present writer has no contribution to make.

Nevertheless, in order to complete our picture of life and to see how certain physical characteristics of living organisms fit in with the definition given in § 33, a short digression into the physics of mechanical stability may not be out of place. In the following pages, therefore, an attempt will be made to epitomize, as clearly as seems possible without the introduction of complicated mathematical formulae and technical terms, the fundamental physical facts which underlie the existence of mechanically stable macroscopic structures in a universe of atoms whose primary occupation is the chaotic motion of thermal agitation.

Mechanical stability is not the only form of physical stability found in the living organism, but since it is at the root of the organism's solidity, it is the only one which is relevant in an analysis of the basic phenomenon of life. Other forms of stability may be relevant in discussing particular physical or chemical processes in a living organism, but they have no primary relevance in the very general context of our analysis.

Living organisms, as do inorganic bodies, consist of assemblies of fundamental, atomic, particles whose dynamical behaviour is determined by (a) the essentially chaotic motion of thermal agitation and, (b) the classical and quantum effects of electrostatic forces between the particles, which result in mutual attraction, repulsion, dipole moments, &c. As far as the fundamental particles of living organisms are concerned, we may regard atoms in different states of ionization (for simplicity the normal atom will here be regarded as in a state of 'neutral' ionization) as the permanent and indestructible population of our assemblies. The number of atoms per living cell is of the order of magnitude of 10^{12} or 10^{13}, the number of cells in, say, a small mammal being, in turn, of a similar order.

Any large assembly of atoms has at any time a certain total energy and is capable of existing at any time in any one of a large number of discrete, so-called 'accessible' states of internal motion (or, in the language of quantum physics, 'energy eigenfunctions'); this number depends on the different, physically possible ways of distributing the total energy of the assembly over its individual members, and on the different states of motion of each member which are compatible with its energy. During their chaotic heat motion collisions or close approximations between the particles may take place, resulting in energy transfers or ionization changes.

The statement that the heat motion of the fundamental particles is chaotic, means that all the accessible states of motion of the assembly are equally probable, and hence that the probability of any given mode of distribution of the total energy of the assembly over the particles is proportional to the number of possible ways of realizing it in the assembly. To take an imaginary and highly simplified example, assume that a given assembly of atoms consists of five atoms only, each capable of existing only in two states of motion, these states being characterized by the energy e_1 and e_2 respectively. Then, since there are $\dfrac{5!}{2!\,3!}$ ways of realizing a mode of distribution of the total energy of the assembly in which two atoms are in the state e_1 and three in the state e_2, the probability of the occurrence of that particular mode of distribution of the total energy is proportional to $\dfrac{5!}{2!\,3!}$.

As far as the heat motion of our atoms is concerned, all the possible ways of realizing any particular distribution of the heat energy of a given assembly are equally probable, so that the number, W, of ways of realizing the most probable distribution of the energy may, for large assemblies, be taken as an index of the degree of chaos or disorder existing within the assembly. For in the case of large assemblies, the most probable distribution of the energy is so overwhelmingly more probable than any other that we may usually assume it to be realized. A certain thermodynamical quantity S, called the *entropy*, can be shown to be proportional to the logarithm of this number W, and is therefore generally taken as an index of the disorder which exists in any given assembly of atoms. Thus we may write $S = k \log W$, where k is the constant of proportionality ('Boltzmann's constant': $k = 1 \cdot 371 \cdot 10^{-16}$).

The nature of S as a thermodynamical variable may be exemplified by the following physical facts.

In isolated physical systems the value of S, and hence the disorder of the system, can only increase; it never decreases. The maximum amount of work a given system of atoms can do on its surroundings (if these remain at constant temperature) i.e. the so-called *free energy* of the system, is related to the total energy U of the system by the relation $F = U - TS$, where F is the free energy and T the (absolute) temperature of the assembly. (Since 'work' in this classical physical context is a macroscopic concept and refers, therefore, only to concerted and orderly actions of the atoms, this relation may be taken roughly to mean that the energy which is free for concerted atomic activities is equal to the total energy of the system minus that proportion which is involved in disconcerted or chaotic atomic activities.)

So much about the disorder reigning in any assembly of atomic particles. Our next question must be how some enduring form of geometrical order can arise from this chaos and how atomic particles whose natural leaning, so to speak, is towards chaotic agitation, nevertheless come to arrange themselves into orderly and mechanically stable structures, such as molecules, crystals, elastic fibrils, membranes, tissue- and nerve-fibres, &c.

The main responsibility for this order and stability rests with the electrostatic forces of interaction between atomic particles or between groups of atomic particles. Wherever there are physical forces potentially capable of doing work there is energy in the form of so-called potential energy. And the existence of the electrostatic forces of interaction between the particles of our assemblies means that a certain fraction of the total energy of any selected assembly of atoms exist in the form of potential energy—energy, in other words, which is tied down and, since it is not kinetic energy, to which no states of motion correspond. The natural tendency of the assembly towards disorder and towards that condition in which the greatest number of states of motion are accessible to the system, will cause it to behave in such a way as to minimize that fraction of the total energy which is bound up as potential energy. Paradoxically enough, this is precisely what leads to the existence of order; since for any selected set of atoms it may happen, and often does happen, that the electrostatic interactions cause the potential energy of the set to be such a function of the atoms' mutual positional relationships that there exist one or more orderly configuration of these particles for which the potential energy of the set will be a minimum. Such a set will accordingly be characterized by the existence of one or more well-ordered configurations of preferred positions, relative loci, or orientations for its members, and if the respective energy 'troughs' are of sufficient depth we must expect to find these atoms over shorter or longer periods of time (depending on the magnitude of the disturbing influences to which they are subject—not excluding their own thermal agitation) tidily arranged according to these preferred positions, loci, or orientations. They will thus come to form a well-ordered configuration which is mechanically stable in the sense that it will resist disturbances and will automatically resume its normal shape after deformation, provided that neither the disturbing forces nor the deformations are too large. The thermal agitation of the respective atoms will not be lost by this emergence of order, but will become modified into random oscillations around the fixed positions, loci, or orientations of the configuration.

For instance, the potential energy E_p of the electrostatic interaction between two atoms A and B may be the following type of function of their distance D:

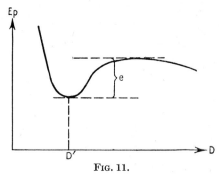

FIG. 11.

Within its neighbourhood D' will then be the most probable average distance between A and B, and once these two atoms have chanced to come into such close approximation they will stay this average distance apart over longer or shorter periods according to the 'rupture energy' e of this 'bond' between them (Fig. 11), i.e. according to the amount of energy which must be applied to lift them out of the energy trough. This rupture energy may therefore be taken as a rough measure of the stability of the bond. It may happen to be supplied to the system through thermal agitation, mechanical agitation, electron transfer, or through electrical forces involved in collisions of A or B with other atoms. Generally speaking, therefore, the existence of some such potential energy minima may cause sets of atoms to arrange themselves in more or less complex equilibrium configurations whose stability will vary with the magnitude of the rupture energy; and it is in this general manner that well-ordered and stable structural complexes of atoms arise from the fundamental disorder of atomic assemblies.

The average lifetime of a given structural complex of atoms

depends on two factors: the magnitude of its rupture energy, and the constitution and temperature of its environment, i.e. on the nature and energy of other atoms or complexes impinging upon it. Independent structural complexes of atoms whose average lifetime is large in an environment consisting of exactly similar complexes at temperatures accessible to experimenters, i.e. molecules, are of unique importance for the practical chemist because, in principle at least, they can be isolated in bulk. This property is perhaps the most important property in chemical laboratory practice. But from the purely theoretical biological point of view, and from the viewpoint of one who wishes to understand the general nature of life rather than interfere with its chemical progress, a preoccupation with the idea of 'molecules' may do more harm than good. For matter in bulk which is homogeneous in the above sense is the exception rather than the rule in living matter: it has too low a level of organization. In so far as living systems owe some part of their independence from the environment to the mechanical stability of their structures, and the rest to directively correlated activities, i.e. one part to stability, the other part to instability (cf. § 43); and in so far as all degrees of stability or instability are equally important to life, any preoccupation of this kind with just one form of stability may well tend to distort our perspective. The concept of 'molecule' can mislead because, in drawing a line across the scale of stabilities of atomic complexes, it is guided by extraneous practical reasons unrelated to the intrinsic nature of life.

For much the same reason that atoms aggregate into more or less stable structural complexes, such complexes may in turn combine into larger and more comprehensive equilibrium configurations, and these larger complexes may again show greater or less stability according to the rupture energies of their bonds. They will defy deformation for the same reason as before: any deviation from their equilibrium configuration entails an increase in the potential energy of the system at the expense of the number of accessible states of internal (heat) motion and at the expense, therefore, of the system's entropy.

In this manner are built up the large folded protein chains of elastic fibres, networks, membranes, and other structures within living organisms. The larger these structures are, the less dependent do they tend to become on the presence within them of any one particular atom or atomic group. Quick exchange or even temporary absence of one or more atoms or groups within such large equilibrium configurations may occur without entailing a collapse of the configuration. The identity of such a large complex, in other words, may outlast the identity of its components: the enduring thing is no longer a given aggregate of particles but an abstract pattern of preferred positions for them. We may speak of such structures as 'dynamic structures'. Most macroscopic organic structures are of this type. Dynamic structures are known already at the molecular level. For instance, any hydrogen atom of an organic acid which is not directly attached to a carbon atom (e.g. the hydrogen atom in —OH and —COOH groups) is very 'labile' and readily exchanges with the hydrogen atoms of the water. In recent times investigations with isotopes have shown strikingly how very readily the atoms in even the most vitally important tissues of living organisms are currently exchanged for others of their kind.

All matter at temperatures above absolute zero involves ceaseless activity on the atomic scale because of the thermal agitation of its atomic components. But, as a rule, living systems show ceaseless activity also on a higher and macroscopic scale, and they differ in this respect from the majority of solid or semi-solid inorganic objects. Has this anything to do with the fact that they depend for their existence on directive correlation?

Now there is nothing in the concept of directive correlation as such which necessarily implies macroscopic change and activity. A macroscopic physical variable can remain in a continuous directive correlation to another macroscopic variable during a given time interval without necessarily having to undergo any change during that interval. For instance, if a man keeps a searchlight trained on a fixed object we may have a directive correlation involving no actual variation of the variables concerned. The variations of the coenetic variables and of the directively correlated variables to which the definition of directive correlation refers, are merely hypothetical variations; they are not variations in time: no time derivative enters into our definition of directive correlation (cf. § 20).

In what circumstances then will the existence of directive correlation between physical variables imply actual variations in time of the directively correlated variables? The answer is, that such actual variations in time will be implied if there exists a directive correlation throughout a finite interval of time and if the coenetic variable undergoes actual variations in time which remain within the 'maximum variations' of this directive correlation. For in that case some of the hypothetical variations of the coenetic variable are realized in time. They have come to life, so to speak; and the variations of the directively correlated variables which are implied by the above variations of the coenetic variable, will also become actual variations in time. This bears on the present question as follows. The coenetic variables of many directive correlations within living systems are environmental variables. But the environment of living organisms is perpetually subject to real macroscopic changes and fluctuations. Many of these coenetic variables accordingly undergo real variations in time and the existence of the respective directive correlations throughout finite intervals of time will thus entail active changes in the organism. In other words, from our definition of a living organism it follows that in so far as living organisms are adapted to environments that are not strictly uniform in time we must expect them to be dynamic systems. This does not mean that every activity of the organism is necessitated by time-variations of some environmental coenetic variable. But it does mean that our definition of a living organism precludes systems which are completely static throughout the whole of their existence in an environment that is subject to macroscopic changes in time.

The concept of 'energy' is a classical illustration of the fact that the crucial difference between philosophical speculation and exact science lies in the precision of the concepts used. While in biology 'vital' energies, 'nervous' energies, and the like have often been invoked as vague speculative concepts without yielding anything resembling a scientific theory, the physicist who insists on accurate quantitative definitions found in his energy concepts the key of some of his most important theories. The subject of our present discussion is one of these physical energy concepts. The so-called free energy F of a system of atoms or other fundamental particles is, as we know, defined as that portion of the system's total energy U which can be converted into work done by the system on its surroundings, and it is related to the total energy U by the relation $F = U - TS$, where S is the entropy of the system and T its absolute temperature.

It has just been shown that the continuous directive correlation of living systems to changing environmental circumstances involves them in continuous macroscopic activities. Now, in so far as this macroscopic activity takes the form of work done by the organism, or any part of it, on its external or internal environment, it implies the existence of a corresponding amount of free energy. It is thus seen that the existence of continuous directive correlations in living organisms as a rule requires a certain minimum free-energy content.

The ultimate source of this free energy is solar radiation. But when solar radiation strikes the earth it will deliver free energy only under special circumstances. The normal effect of solar radiation is merely to raise the temperature of the objects it strikes, and most of the energy delivered will therefore be in the form of kinetic, i.e. chaotic heat energy. The total energy of the objects will rise but their entropy will increase concomitantly and, since $F = U - TS$, their free energy may increase only by insignificant amounts. Under special circumstances however, such entropy increases may be considerably delayed in favour of correspondingly greater free energy increases. This is the thermodynamic significance of chlorophyll-containing plants. The chlorophyll-coated chloroplasts of these plants can use the energy of the sun for the synthesis of carbohydrates and, in thus building up orderly compounds and retarding entropy increases, increase their free-energy content. With the partial exception of the autotrophic bacteria, we have here the fundamental organic source of the free energy of the plant and animal kingdom. Stored in the direct and derived products of photosynthesis, the free energy is distributed during the metabolism of the plants or of the animals which feed upon them to those sites of biological activity where it is required, and there it is released by the respective physiological oxidations, fermentations, osmotic activities, &c.

According to the Second Law of Thermodynamics the overall free-energy content of any isolated physical system must decrease during any finite process the system may undergo. A corollary of this is that the overall entropy of the isolated system must increase. The net effect of the chlorophyll-containing plants in the universe as a whole is that they retard the ultimately inevitable decrease of the free energy contained in the sun's radiation, and retard the corresponding entropy increases. The animal kingdom, on the other hand, directly or indirectly draws its free energy from that of the plants and by utilizing it in its own metabolism accelerates the free-energy decrease and entropy increase in the universe. Neither the one nor the other physical effect can be used as a thermodynamic criterion for life, because inorganic systems, too, may cause such retardations or accelerations (e.g. the water cycle in nature). Nor can any living organism create an exception to the Second Law by causing a decrease in the entropy of an isolated physical system of which it may be part. On the other hand, there is much to be said for using these thermodynamical relationships in drawing a boundary between the plant and the animal kingdoms.

§ 42. *The Nature of Biological Progress*

The failure of science to analyse those organizational relationships in living nature which transcend the levels of molecular

organization meant not only that science fell short of understanding the real nature of life but also that it was bound to
fail in any attempt to discover precise grounds on which a distinction could be drawn between higher and lower forms of
life, and on which a precise notion of biological progress could
be erected.

The traditional idea of *biological progress* broadly implies
that living organisms possess certain attributes which (*a*) are
general characteristics of life; (*b*) admit of quantitative comparison and hence enable living organisms to be arranged
along a scale according to the degree to which they possess
these attributes; (*c*) in some sense possess biological value and
justify the classification of organisms as 'higher' or 'lower'
according to their approximate position on this scale; (*d*) have
shown an overall tendency to increase in the course of evolution, and (*e*) on the human level stand in some direct relation
to moral values. Is there any objective foundation in nature
for this idea and, if so, can it be given a precise formulation?
The subject of biological progress has never been free from
major confusions of thought and it will be worth while to see
how far the results of our analysis will go to remove some of
them.

Any scientific examination of evolution which fails through
ignorance to take into account the fundamental abstract characteristics of life and the fundamental relationships involved in
vital organization, is bound to fail in trying to detect criteria
which will satisfy these five conditions. Many biologists, notably
mechanists, have thus been driven to the mistaken conclusion
that there exists no objective ground in evolution to justify
the notion of biological progress in the above sense. The nearest
attribute they were able to detect in living organisms which
approaches the conditions (*a*)–(*e*) is, perhaps, that of structural complexity. In the broad sense this satisfies (*a*), (*b*), and
(*d*) but, of course, it fails completely over (*c*) and (*e*). It
also invites such vexing questions as whether the complexity of a loosely integrated locust swarm is not just as great
as that of a highly integrated ant colony, and whether the

complexity of a dead animal is not just as great as that of a living animal.

While these biologists lean towards a rather uncompromising denial of biological progress, others have fallen back on vaguer concepts and maintain that something corresponding to the traditional idea of progress can indeed be found in evolution and that (provided one was not too critical about the concepts used) this something could satisfactorily be formulated in terms of (say) increased adaptability, control over environment, success, independence from environment, self-regulation, social integration, &c. They argue that although isolated strands of evolutionary development have often shown a partial decline of any or all of these attributes, it is, nevertheless, an overriding and undeniable fact, that the broad stream of evolution has been accompanied by a progressive and very marked increase in the degree to which these attributes can be found among the living forms of any given epoch. It is also clear that the above attributes go far to satisfy (*a*), (*b*), and (*c*). But their relation to (*e*) has always been obscure and this problem certainly was not solved by the procrustean solution adopted by some modern biologists of simply identifying ethical progress with evolutionary progress.

In this unsatisfactory state the question of biological progress has remained an impasse for some time. As happens so often, this discord betokens merely the vagueness of the concepts used. Take, for instance, the concept of adaptation. The fact that some biologists maintain that higher organisms are better adapted to their environment than lower organisms, while other biologists hold that a bacillus, a jellyfish, or a tapeworm is as well adapted to its environment as a bird, an ant, or Man, indicates little else than that the concept is being used in different senses.[1] The same applies when we find one biologist speaking about the control exerted by an organism over its environment while his colleague, with equal conviction, asserts that it is the environment which always controls the

---

[1] In the first case 'adaptation' is used in the full sense of directive correlation, in the second case in the diluted sense of 'appropriateness'.

organism; or when one biologist sees progress in the organism's increased independence of the environment while another maintains that the progressive increase in the social integration of living organisms implies a corresponding decrease in their individual independence.

The question of biological progress is thus seen to be another example in which everything hinges on the accuracy of definitions. Once again the exact concept of directive correlation can be of use. For if we examine the particular sense in which such attributes of living matter as adaptability, control, independence, integration, self-regulation, &c. may rightly be regarded as criteria of biological progress we realize in each case that it is the very sense in which they refer to that purpose-like character of life processes which we have analysed in terms of directive correlation. Only in this sense, for instance, do adaptation, integration, coordination, &c. indeed admit of degrees of accomplishment, and the growth of these degrees reflect the fundamental trend of biological evolution. What, in fact, distinguishes the higher organisms from lower forms is their increased power to maintain their existence, and safeguard their future, in the face of contingent and often adverse environmental fluctuations by means of adaptive, regulative, coordinated, and integrated activities in the sense of the preceding sections, i.e. by activities which are in some, usually integrated manner, directively correlated to one another and to their environment. The increased adaptability of higher organisms is the increased degree and range (§ 20) of the directive correlation (especially short-term directive correlation) between their actions and their environment; their increased self-regulation is the increased degree and range of directively correlated and integrated activities of the type discussed in §§ 32 and 33; their increased control over the environment is the increased power to influence their environment by directively correlated activities; their increased independence of the environment is that independence which their survival—the ultimate focal condition of many of their directively correlated activities—enjoys from environmental

coenetic variables (§ 14); finally, their increased social integration represents an increase of the degree and range of
directive correlations of the type discussed in § 40. In short,
biological progress lies in the growing extent and degree to which
the power of living organisms (or their societies) to hold their
own in the face of contingent and often adverse environmental
changes and to safeguard their future, has become enhanced
by directive correlations (especially short-term correlations) of
the life processes to one another and to the environment. This,
no doubt, is what is meant when people speak vaguely of
progress as being essentially an 'intensification' of life.

It remains to show that this interpretation of biological
progress in terms of the growth of the degree and range of
directive correlation satisfies the conditions (*b*)–(*e*) cited above.
Condition (*b*) is satisfied by the concept of directive correlation
in several ways because we know that there are several ways
in which we may distinguish different degrees of directive
correlation (§ 20). Since directive correlation was shown to
be the characteristic spatio-temporal system property which
underlies the organism's independence of the environment and
underlies the fact that its survival is not merely accidental,
(*c*) is obviously satisfied; and as to (*d*), there can be no doubt
that the degree and extent of directive correlation in living
nature has shown an overall tendency to increase in the course
of evolution.

The discussion of condition (*e*) is not very easy if we are
to avoid digressions into moral philosophy which would be out
of place in this work; yet, I think this much can be said.
Whatever particular theory one may hold about the ultimate
nature of moral values and foundation of ethics, most people
will agree that it is part of the essence of moral behaviour that
such behaviour should conduce to the growth of harmonious
and peaceful social relationships; or to be more precise, an
essential ingredient of moral behaviour is an attitude of
unselfishness, which causes the individual to consider the
needs of the community in the daily run of things and thus
favours the growth of social harmony and peace. (I am not

asserting that this is the ultimate justification of moral behaviour, but merely that it is part of the essence of moral behaviour to be a contributory force to social integration.) Now from an objective point of view the growth of social harmony and peaceful relationships in an integrated society *ceteris paribus* implies the growth of mutual adjustment and adaptation between the members of the society, between their activities and attitudes towards one another. Hence moral progress implies the growth of the range and degrees of the directive correlations existing between the members. We see therefore that, so far as these extremely general remarks go, our interpretation of biological progress shows it to be intimately connected with moral progress. Although moral progress need not actually be identified with biological progress, we can nevertheless say that it favours certain forms of biological progress, and that it is a necessary condition for some of them. Condition (*e*), therefore, may also be regarded as satisfied by our interpretation of biological progress as the continuous growth of the degrees and ranges of directive correlation in nature.[1]

It is not necessary here to survey the whole course of evolution and to illustrate in detail how the part played by directive correlation in the self-preservation of the organism grew in importance with the progressive emergence and development of higher forms of life. But it will not be amiss to make a few observations about the most recent product of this evolutionary process: Man.

The evolution of Man is marked by a number of special features, some of which have already been mentioned:

(i) As far as the internal regulations of his body are concerned there is no very remarkable departure from his evolutionary ancestors. In contrast, his power directively to correlate his behaviour to his environment shows a unique increase. This is mainly due to the development of rational thought and speech, and the growth of knowledge which this has made

---

[1] It is worth pointing out that this interpretation of biological progress agrees well with the theological conception of progress as the development of wider and more accomplished personalities.

possible. The relation between rational behaviour and directive correlation was discussed in § 35 and requires no further
comment in the present context.

(ii) The degree of social coordination and integration of
which Man has become capable is also unparalleled in the
animal kingdom. Although there exist high degrees of social
integration in insect societies, these are far surpassed by the
power of human beings to coordinate their behaviour with their
fellow men, particularly so far as short- and medium-term directive correlations are concerned. This aspect of human evolution
has also been dealt with earlier on.

(iii) Man has acquired a unique power to organize his inorganic environment, to build and use technical instruments
as means towards his ends. These range from simple tools to
the industrial machines, mechanical transport, &c., of our own
technical age. Lotka has coined the convenient term 'exoso-
matic evolution' for this development in the evolution of Man;
it may be contrasted with 'endosomatic evolution'.[1]

This power of Man to organize his inorganic environment
by the construction and use of instruments and machines, is
essentially a power to introduce directive correlation into
the environment. Yet, the type of directive correlation here
involved may not be at once obvious to the reader. It is
mainly of two kinds, the one pertains to the immediate use of
an instrument, the other to its construction.

If a monkey uses a stick as an instrument for, let us say,
pulling a banana into its cage, then, throughout that act, not
only the movements of its arm are directively correlated to the
position of the banana, but also the movements of the stick.
In other words, while an inorganic object is being used by
a living agent as an *instrument* towards a certain end, there
exist short-term directive correlations between the instrument
and the environment, and these directive correlations between
inorganic objects have been introduced by the agent. The
power to use technical instruments is therefore a power to

[1] The terms speak for themselves: see A. J. Lotka (1945), *Human Biology*,
vol. xvii, pp. 167–94.

introduce directive correlations of this kind into the inorganic environment.

The case is a little more complicated when the instrument first has to be constructed, as in the case of industrial machines. The process of constructing a machine—as does indeed any *creative* activity—involves a high degree of directive correlation even in simple cases, and it is also a process in the course of which the agent introduces directive correlations into his inorganic environment. For, while an instrument or machine undergoes construction, not only the activities of the designer and manufacturer are directively correlated to one another or to the environment, but also the changes which the materials or parts of the instrument or machine undergo in the process of manufacture, assembly, and fitting. Moreover, as long as the machine or instrument remains in working order, and as long as our conception of it as a physical system comprises the whole of its history, including the period of its construction,[1] its parts remain directively correlated to one another even after it has been completed. It is characteristic of any *created* object that it is the outcome of directively correlated activities; that, provided it undergoes no destructive changes afterwards, there continue to exist directive correlations between its parts which have coenetic variables in the period of its creation; and that these directive correlations are derived from the activities of its creator.

(iv) The fourth and last feature in the evolution of Man which we shall consider, is one which cannot be discussed in detail without introducing definite hypotheses and theories about the nature of the phenomena concerned, which would be out of keeping with the purely analytical aims of this work. Nevertheless, it is a feature that is so often raised in discussions about human progress that a few words about it may not be out of place even if they have to remain vague and general.

We have pointed to the relation which exists between the idea of moral progress and our interpretation of biological

---

[1] Because this is the period which contains the coenetic variables of the directive correlations concerned.

progress. We saw that the biological significance of moral progress lies in the part played by the moral nature of Man in bringing about higher degrees of integration and directive correlation in human society. These thoughts may have set the reader wondering whether the two other factors that distinguish Man in the same spiritual sphere from lower forms of life, viz. his *religious sense* and *sense of beauty*, have a similar biological significance. We are here, of course, on extremely difficult ground and most of the questions involved are outside the scope of this book. But in one or two respects the evolutionary development of Man's religious and aesthetic sense does, in the present context, appear significant in a way which it may be worth while to point out.

Our investigation and analysis of the goal-directed aspects of nature touches theology in several ways. For one thing, religion is very largely concerned with just these teleological aspects of nature and human destiny. In having shown that it is possible to describe these teleological aspects of nature in terms of mathematical relations between physical variables, and in having thus shown that these aspects represent *physical* relationships as genuine and real as, say, gravity or magnetism, we have not given substance to any particular religious beliefs, but we *can* claim to have given substance to some of the particular things religious beliefs are about. Again, the results of our analysis bear on theology in that the question whether the existence of God is compatible with the results of physical science, revolves primarily around the question whether a purposive determination of events in nature is compatible with the causal determination postulated by the physical sciences. Our analysis has shown in what sense these two forms of determination are entirely compatible.

But these particular theological questions do not concern us here. What does concern us at the moment is whether the progressive development of Man's religious beliefs and attitudes of mind is a significant human phenomenon in our interpretation of biological progress. Having identified biological progress with the evolutionary growth of the range and degree of directive correlation (especially of the 'short-term' kind) to be found in living nature, we must ask whether we can look upon the gradual evolution of Man's religious beliefs from primitive tribal cults to (say) the essentially universal religion of Christianity as an integral part of his biological progress.

I think there are several closely related grounds on which this question can be answered in the affirmative.

In the first place, it can be claimed that the transition from tribal deities, and from tribal or national idolatry, to a universal religion preaching goodwill between all men, is one which *ceteris paribus* tends to favour the overall and long-term growth of social harmony and integration in the world, and *ipso facto*, therefore, tends to favour the overall and long-term growth of directive correlation in human society. It is true, of course, that periods of fanatical nationalism and national idolatry may achieve within the nation a truly unique degree of co-operation and social integration, but for the world at large this merely represents a localized and temporary expansion of the social forms of directive correlation. The overall and long-term effect on the total degree of social integration in the world is bound to be negative.

Secondly, there is a certain sense in which one can say that a true religion leads to wider and more accomplished personalities, and in which this implies an increase in the adjustment (hence, directive correlation) of the individual to both his living and non-living environment.

Finally, I think it can be said that the religious beliefs of Man, whatever their particular nature, are based on a definite awareness of the widespread existence of goal-directed activities in nature, and of their fundamental importance for all forms of life. That is to say, at the root of Man's religious beliefs lies an intuitive awareness (however inarticulate this may be) that all life and particularly human life (the health and destiny of society as well as of the individual) ultimately depends on the existence or occurrence of a multitude of integrated directive correlations; that the vast majority of

these directive correlations as such are not of human author-
ship and entirely beyond human control: while Man can often
destroy directive correlations, e.g. by killing, he cannot usually
at will make or re-make them; and, indeed, that Man is totally
ignorant about the precise laws which govern them, i.e. the
precise laws which govern the appearance or disappearance,
growth or decline of particular directive correlations, social or
individual, at particular times and places in nature.

Seen in this light the religious beliefs of Man reflect essentially the sense of humility and dependence which he derives
from this situation and represent the mental adjustment he
makes to it. From a purely biological point of view our religious beliefs thus appear to be of the nature of an adjustment,
not to any concrete set of environmental circumstances, but
to the universal existence (and fundamental importance for
life) of the abstract property of directive correlation as such.
In short, our religious beliefs might be described biologically
as an *adaptation to the fact of adaptation.* In this respect it
is obvious that the development of Man's religious beliefs is
a significant phenomenon in our interpretation of biological
progress.

In conclusion, a word about Man's 'sense of beauty', that
is to say, about the biological phenomenon that certain formal
properties in the outward appearance of objects in his environment can provoke in him certain feelings *sui generis,* which are
not based on the practical usefulness of the object, and which,
although somehow analogous to moral feelings are yet impossible to be confused with them. Here again little can be said
without introducing special hypotheses and theories, which
would be out of keeping with the aims of this book. Nor can
we fall back on any generally accepted theory about the
nature of these feelings *sui generis,* or about the question
whether they are provoked by objective characteristics common
to all objects of aesthetic excellence. There does exist, however, some consensus of opinion among philosophers that most
objects of beauty have one important property in common,
although individual opinions differ on whether this property

can be called 'objective' and whether it is a significant factor in actually provoking the feeling Man experiences in perceiving them. This property is the following. The outward appearance of a beautiful object nearly always conveys the immediate impression of having a particular formal and purposive unity. Irrespective of whether it is a work of art, such as a painting, or an object of natural beauty such as a flower, the mere sensory perception of an object of beauty always conveys the immediate impression that it is a whole in which a number of perceived parts occupy purposively assigned positions and have purposively assigned formal relations. That is to say, in beholding a beautiful object we always have a strong sensory impression of purposiveness; we feel, immediately and without reflection, that we are confronted with a whole consisting of parts whose mutual relations were not determined by 'efficient' causes but by 'final' causes. Except in 'functional beauty', however, this impression is not as a rule accompanied by any impression of the particular nature of the 'final' causes concerned. In other words, *a beautiful object always gives the general impression of being a whole whose parts are directively correlated*, although this does not as a rule include an impression of the nature of the focal condition.

If these very general remarks are correct, the existence of a sense of beauty in Man and his innate tendency to feel attracted by beautiful objects, at once acquires significance in our interpretation of biological progress. For it then means that in the course of evolution Man has acquired an innate tendency to feel attracted by those objects in his environment whose sensory appearance suggests the existence of directive correlations between their parts. Now the existence of this innate tendency in Man may of course be no more than an incidental concomitant of the fact that in the course of evolution Man has acquired an innate capacity of being aware of directive correlations in his environment and some intuitive knowledge of the significance of these relationships for life and for the harmonious integration of the individual with his living or non-living environment. But it is difficult to avoid the impression that there is more to it, and that the existence of a sense of beauty in Man, and of an instinctive desire to be surrounded by beautiful objects, i.e. by objects whose sensory appearance suggests the existence of directive correlations between their parts, fulfils a definite biological function by promoting the degree of organic integration which the individual achieves in his relation to the environment. It does not seem too bold to assume that such an instinctive desire is part of a general psychological mechanism whose function is to lead the individual to the most organic parts of the environment, or rather to those parts in which there exist the greatest concentration of directive correlation and which offer, therefore, the greatest opportunity for the coming into existence of higher levels of organic integration between him and the environment.

If a further examination of this hypothesis should prove it to be acceptable the evolutionary development of a sense of beauty in Man would at once stand revealed as an integral part of his biological progress.

§ 43. *Retrospect.*

The last chapters have taken us from the formal analysis of simple instances of purposiveness in nature to an analysis of all those abstract properties that are most truly characteristic of living systems and their organization, i.e. to an analysis of the abstract properties of life as such. We may accordingly consider our main task to have been accomplished. But it would be unwise to stop at this point without glancing once more over our results and setting them into a proper perspective. In particular, more must be said about the part played by mathematics in this analysis and about the general gains we have derived from its application. These gains are at once the most important and yet the most difficult to discern at a first reading of the book. In spite of all that was said in Chapter I, more than one reader at the end of Chapter III will have asked himself, What have we gained? or, Where do we go from here? Mathematical symbolism has been put

to an unwonted use here and our mathematical results are unlikely to help the mathematician solve existing mathematical
problems or help the practical scientist with existing practical ones. Yet I maintain that the mathematical part of this
book has yielded a very profound gain. The reason for this
paradox is that the type of problems which our mathematical
analysis illuminates are predominantly problems which, precisely because they have never before been formulated in terms
of mathematical relations between physical variables, have
traditionally been classified as philosophical and metaphysical
problems rather than scientific ones. By showing that they
can be formulated mathematically our analysis has converted
them from a species of the former into a species of the latter,
although they are still, of course, problems unlikely to have
preoccupied the mathematician or scientist who chances to
take up this book.

Let me preface a further discussion of these matters by a
short summary of some of our main results:

The main instrument we have developed for analysing
the purposiveness of vital activities and the abstract organizational relationships which distinguish living systems from
inorganic objects, is the concept of *directive correlation*. In
Chapter III it was demonstrated that, in principle, this concept can be formulated in terms of mathematical relations
between physical variables. It was shown that this could be
done, for instance, in a restricted sense in which certain functions were assumed to be differentiable, but, if required, also
in a general sense in which no such restrictions were imposed.
In either case we had to distinguish between 'directively correlated' variables, 'coenetic' variables, and 'focal' variables.

In the subsequent chapters it was shown how this concept of directive correlation could be used to analyse, and to express without loss of meaning, all the most essential aspects of
vital organization, purposiveness, or goal-directed activities in
nature. The most important explications arrived at in this
manner were the following:

Degree and range of directive correlation. By these we have come to understand the scope of a given directive correlation as indicated by the maximum permissible range of coenetic variation and by the number of correlated[1] variables respectively (§ 20).

Adaptation. The value of a biological variable is 'adapted' to the value of another variable if both variables are directively correlated and an antecedent value of the latter variable figures as a coenetic variable in this correlation (§ 13).

Coordination. A set of biological activities are 'coordinated' if they are directively correlated and if each activity also plays the part of a coenetic variable in at least one of the directive correlations concerned (§ 31).

Regulation. The most characteristic case of a biological 'regulation' is the case of a directive correlation in which the focal condition consists of the maintenance of one or more physiological variables at a constant value (§ 32).

Organic integration. A set of organic activities is 'integrated' in the biological sense if the activities are directively correlated and if these correlations themselves are again directively correlated *inter se* (e.g. if their respective focal conditions may in turn be regarded as a set of directively correlated variables) (§ 35).

Self-preservation. The activities of a living organism have a 'self-preserving' character in that they are connected by a set of directive correlations which has as ultimate focal condition the continued existence of the organism throughout a finite span of time (§ 35).

Living organism. A living organism may be described as a compact physical system of mechanically connected parts whose states and activities are related by an integrated set of directive correlations which, over and above any proximate focal condition, have the continued existence of the system as an ultimate focal condition. *Death* may be

---

[1] In all these explications it is important to remember that we are using the term 'correlation' in the sense of 'one-one correspondence' and *not* in the sense of a 'statistical correlation'.

described as the breakdown of these directive correlations (§ 33).

Instinctive and learnt behaviour. Animal behaviour is 'instinctive' if it is primarily an instance of short-term and *long*-term directive correlations (§ 30). 'Learnt' behaviour, on the other hand, is behaviour that is primarily an instance of short-term and *medium*-term directive correlations (§ 37).

Integrated social units. An association of living organisms is an 'integrated social unit' or 'society' if there exists a system of integrated directive correlations between the states or activities of the members which has the continued existence of the association as an ultimate focal condition (§ 40).

Biological progress. We identify 'biological progress' with the observed tendency in nature gradually to evolve biological forms whose self-preservation is based on ever larger degrees and ranges of directive correlation (especially short-term correlations). We regard the development of aesthetic, moral, and religious faculties in Man as intimately connected with this process (§ 42).

It will be seen from this survey that all the main concepts concerned with vital organization and the general nature of life are capable of being defined in terms of directive correlation and, since we have shown the latter concept to be definable in terms of mathematical relations between physical variables, we can claim to have shown that all the most distinctive features of observed life as a whole can be formulated and analysed in terms of such mathematical relationships and can thus be brought into a clear-cut formal relation to the physical sciences.

Now let me attempt to summarize briefly what we have gained by this formal analysis and, in particular, by having shown that it can be reduced to mathematical terms.

In the first place, by clarifying the purposive and organizational relationships which distinguish vital activities we have gained new insight into the general nature of life and have

enabled those philosophers and scientists who are interested
in life as a whole (as distinct from isolated physico-chemical
events occurring within a living organism) and in the teleological aspects of nature, to achieve that mathematical rigour
of thought which may be indispensable if their arguments are
to escape vagueness, ambiguity, and inconclusiveness. In the
philosophy of life and teleology this discipline of thought has
never been observed. Volume upon volume has been written
about the general nature of life and about the general relation
between causation and purposiveness in nature; yet, in spite
of all the personal insight and wisdom that has gone into these
writings, no definite theory has emerged. For, with only a
few exceptions, no problem was precisely formulated and no
rigorous discipline of thought conformed to.

The fact that we have illustrated how the main concepts
relating to the most distinctive characteristics of life may be
translated without loss of meaning into mathematical terms
will, I hope, help to change this trend. The exact relation
between purposiveness, causality, and probability in nature
can now be investigated and has already been briefly examined
in this volume. An analysis of the kind we have carried out
enables us to trace the formal implications of statements about
the purposiveness of natural events with mathematical precision and to investigate the compatibility of different concepts.
Thus we have shown in what sense a goal-directed determination of natural events is compatible with their causal determination. This demonstration could not have been carried out
if we had not brought the discussion right down to the actual
formalism used in physics, i.e. to mathematical relations between physical variables. Other inquiries of this kind have
become possible. An important example was given in § 28.
A sequel to Darwin's theory of natural selection which had
a greatly unsettling effect on modern systems of belief was
the view that natural selection is the negation of all purposiveness in evolutionary processes, and hence that Darwin's
theory destroyed the creative element in evolution. Our theory
has disproved this interpretation. Another, rather extreme,

example of the kind of inquiry we have opened up was given in § 39, when we indicated a sense in which the idea of a free and unembodied, yet immanent, spirit would be compatible with the physical and causal picture of the universe.

A second gain is that we can claim to have reconciled mechanism and vitalism, i.e. the two schools of thought which in the history of biology have alternated with each other for the past three centuries. By expressing in the exact language of physics, and hence in the language of the mechanists, those purposive aspects of nature which were the primary concern of the vitalists, we have reconciled both points of view.

Thirdly, by showing that the purposive, goal-directed character of life as a whole is no mystical thing best left to the speculations of the metaphysicist, nor a mere anthropomorphism, but a clear-cut physical property of material systems and susceptible to mathematical analysis, we have brought back into the *science* of biology those abstract teleological aspects of nature which under the influence of mechanistic thought had gradually become almost entirely ignored. It is obviously essential that the biologist should study not only the concrete physico-chemical events occurring within living organisms, but also the abstract properties of life and vital organization as such. Without this, 'biology' remains a misnomer. But how can this be accomplished except by finding suitable scientific concepts? And in order to establish that the new concepts are scientific in the strictest sense of the word it is essential to show that they can, when necessary, be reduced to mathematical relations between physical variables.

In the history of philosophy and biology the question whether biology can be reduced to physics has often occupied the foreground, and it has particularly troubled the minds of writers who aimed at a unified world view or a unified science. We have now shown that such a reduction is, in principle, possible in the sense that the mathematical language of physics can be extended to cover the true characteristics of observed life.

It has been claimed that periods of vitality in philosophy, of progress in the sense of new insight into old problems, have always been periods in which traditional problems are reformulated to admit the application of new methods; periods when the traditional meanings in a branch of learning are cleaned of the moss of ages that had overgrown them; periods when the stage is set for a fresh statement and a purge of presuppositions. If this is true, the lines of investigation we have outlined in this volume will not be barren. Some of the reformulations suggested by our results are drastic and obviously important for philosophy and theology as well as for biology. The question, for instance, whether a given set of natural events follow a purposive development, or whether the development of the universe itself may be regarded as goal-directed, has become the question whether the physical variables describing the given sets of events or the development of the universe satisfy differential equations of the type (10) and (12), § 20.

Pari passu an analysis of the kind we have conducted offers opportunities for new hypotheses in the explanation of natural phenomena, e.g. of animal or human behaviour. Examples of this kind were given at the end of § 42 and other important ones could be added.

Finally I come to what I believe may ultimately prove to be another profound result of our analysis.

Throughout this century both academic philosophy and Man's practical philosophy of life have witnessed a rapid growth of positivism or near-positivistic doctrines. According to this philosophy only the study of empirical facts is fruitful. Experimental science alone can discover truths about reality, and in philosophy as well as in science the mind invites empty verbalism and error if it looses contact with experience or confesses a belief in *a priori* knowledge. Propositions which lack factual content, i.e. which are not in principle verifiable, are said to be devoid of literal significance and, therefore, meaningless. Thus positivism rejects all metaphysical propositions as meaningless.

This is not the place to argue the case either for or against positivism. The introductory sections of this book have clearly established our own position in this respect. We have outlined the conditions which propositions must fulfil if universal agreement about their meaning is to be possible and if they are to avoid both semantic and formal ambiguity or vagueness. But we have been careful to avoid the extreme position of rejecting all propositions that fail to attain these standards as *ipso facto* meaningless, and of rejecting the problems to which they refer as pseudo-problems.

The only point that matters in the present context is that positivism in one form or another has swayed large sections of modern thought. Now this might be a matter of merely academic interest were it not for the fact that according to positivist teaching statements concerning the existence of God and normative ethical and aesthetic judgements lack factual content in the above sense and are therefore to be rejected as meaningless. All this is well known and I need not trace in detail the unsettling influence these trends of thought have had on the moral and religious beliefs of our time. They have given the widespread impression that science and philosophy have destroyed all systems of belief and, alarmed by this development, many writers have come to call for a new synthesis in modern thought, a new integration of knowledge firmly based on the conclusions of science but embodying the essence of religion. The outcome of our mathematical analysis has a considerable significance in this respect. For we have shown that statements about the goal-directedness of events in nature imply statements about mathematical relations between physical variables. Such statements about nature, therefore, have an undeniable factual content. Now it will be generally agreed that statements about the existence of God imply statements about the purposiveness of some natural events. It follows[1] that statements about the existence of God *do* have factual content. Moreover, if we accept the remarks made at the end of § 42 about moral and aesthetic values, a similar argument applies to normative ethical and aesthetic

---

[1] If any statement derivable from a given statement has factual content then the given statement has factual content.

propositions. The positivistic assumption, therefore, that statements about the existence of God and normative ethical and
aesthetic propositions have no factual content (in the sense
used by the positivist) proves to be untenable. It is my belief
that if we follow up these lines of thought we may advance
considerably towards the required synthesis in modern thought
and towards a world-view which combines the conclusions of
science with the essence of religion.

APPENDIX

Directive Correlation and the Quantum Theory

A closed physical system is deterministic if its initial state determines all its subsequent states. That is to say, in a deterministic physical system the value possessed by any state-parameter at any time must be a single-valued function of the initial values of the system's state-parameters. Thus in the example given in § 17, h_t was a single-valued function of h_0 and a_0. A declaration about causal determinism is therefore a declaration about the single-valuedness of certain functional relationships in a closed physical system.

Throughout this work we have assumed that the activities of living organisms are deterministic in this sense. For vital activities on a scale that is large compared with the size of single atomic particles, this hypothesis is fully confirmed by the results of bio-chemistry and biophysics. What happens at the atomic scale is largely irrelevant, because the purpose-like character of vital phenomena is only known to appear on the larger scale. Nevertheless, it is worth while examining whether, in theory at least, purpose-like behaviour is also possible at the atomic level, or whether there is anything in the modern 'quantum' theories of atomic physics that is incompatible with the idea of directive correlation.

In the following pages I propose to give a brief account of what I hold to be the true position of causal determination in atomic systems. At the same time I hope to be able to dispose of the unhappy construction a number of modern authors have given to the so-called 'uncertainty principle' of modern atomic physics in order to support their views about the 'interaction of mind and matter'.

It is well known that the exceedingly abstract mathematical apparatus of the quantum theory has greatly limited the number of scientists other than physicists, and of philosophers, who could acquire a sufficient command of its technical details to form their own opinion about the implications of the theory for their particular branches of inquiry. This situation was aggravated by the fact that the quantum physicists themselves, while agreeing about the formal structure of the theory and the rules for its application, were at a loss to interpret the meaning of their new procedure in terms of traditional concepts and images.

Biological philosophy has come in for its full share of the bold and often misinformed speculation which resulted from this state of affairs. Among the important issues involved in this speculation were the relation between mind and matter, and the allied relation between purposiveness and causal determination in nature. Thus a number of philosophers, still struggling with the concepts of mind and matter in the light of a Cartesian dualism, saw in the 'uncertainty principle' of the quantum theory a gratuitous opportunity to explain how 'mind' or 'purposive agents' could 'act on matter'. Their interpretation of this principle was that atomic events enjoy a freedom of action, or at any rate a freedom from causal determination, which enables 'mind' and 'purposive agents' to influence the course of physical events, and to assert themselves in a physical and otherwise deterministic universe. In so far as our analysis has shown that the antithesis between a purposive and a causal determination of events in nature, which these authors accept as axiomatic, does not in fact exist, their theories have already been refuted. But the idea of directive correlation does presuppose the idea of causal determination, and the question whether atomic events are causally determined or not remains a significant one in our interpretation of life.

The most important postulate of the quantum theory is, that in a system of particles those physical variables which classical physics regarded as measurable[1]—'observables' so called—do not always possess a continuous field of variation but, as a rule, are confined to sets of discrete values. These permitted values are called the 'eigenvalues' of the respective observables.

The remaining postulates of the theory specify conditions which the eigenvalues of any particular observable must fulfil and which enable us to calculate in many cases what values of an observable are eigenvalues and, therefore, possible values; and they prescribe the mathematical operations by means of which the expected mean value of a set of future measurements of an observable, or the expected mean value of the variable in a statistical assembly of similar physical systems, can be calculated from given measurements on the system or on the assembly. The form of prediction specified in the last sentence is the only form which the quantum theory permits.

This limitation of our power of predicting future events in atomic systems give those systems a general appearance of indeterminacy.

---

[1] e.g. the energies, velocities, and positions of the particles.

But if we speak of 'quantum indeterminacy' or 'quantum uncertainty' we usually mean something more specific, viz. Heisenberg's 'uncertainty principle'. Whenever a physical variable cannot be measured with absolute accuracy, any statistical aggregate of measurements of the variable will have a certain 'spread'. The 'standard deviation' may be taken as an index of this spread. Now it follows mathematically from the postulates of the quantum theory that there are certain pairs of observables for which in any aggregate of measurements the standard deviation of the one observable determines a value below which the standard deviation of the other cannot fall. The precise relation is that the product of the standard deviations of any such pair of observables in any aggregate of measurements on a physical system must always equal or exceed a certain finite (although very small) quantity $h/4\pi$, where h is Planck's constant.[1] The more accurately, therefore, we can determine the value of one member of such a pair of observables, the less accurately we can determine the other. Owing to the smallness of h this uncertainty can be neglected in all macroscopic systems but it cannot be neglected in atomic systems. Any position coordinate of a particle together with the associated momentum coordinate are an example of such a pair of incompatible observables.

This uncertainty principle implies that, strictly speaking, even the *idea* of a statistical aggregate of atomic particles in which two such observables have no spread, is incompatible with the postulates of the quantum theory. Moreover, it means that even the idea of a single physical system in which two such variables have definite values, e.g. of an electron with a definite position and definite momentum, is disallowed by the theory.

The consequence of all this for the question of causal determination in atomic systems is that such physical variables as 'position', 'momentum', 'energy', i.e. the observables of classical mechanics, can no longer be regarded as parameters specifying a definite and causally determined state of atomic systems. This, however, does not compel us to abandon the idea of definite and causally determined states in atomic systems. For it still leaves the possibility open of simply rejecting 'energy', 'momentum', 'position', &c. as state-parameters for atomic systems and of introducing new and more satisfactory state-parameters instead. This is, in fact, what the quantum theory has done. It has developed a new conception of the 'state' of an atomic system. In atomic systems the classical

---

[1] $6\cdot55 \times 10^{-27}$ erg sec.

observables are no longer state-parameters but parameters relating to certain types of measuring operations.

In this new conception the 'state' of a physical system is a mathematical construct ϕ whose main properties are the following. First, it can be represented in infinitely many ways by an infinite set of complex numbers, 'expansion coefficients' so called; if the system is time-dependent, each of these coefficients becomes a continuous and single-valued function of the time and each state is a single-valued function of the initial state of the system. The state ϕ therefore fulfils the requirement of causal determination. Secondly, in respect of each classical observable there exists one such representation of the state of a physical system in which each expansion coefficient is associated with one 'eigenvalue'[1] of the observable and in which the square of the modulus of the current value of the expansion coefficient equals the probability that a measurement of the observable will yield the associated eigenvalue. For instance, if $e_1, e_2, e_3, \ldots$ are the eigenvalues of the energy of an atomic system, there exists a representation $b_1, b_2, b_3, \ldots$ of the current 'state' of the system in which $|b_n|^2$ equals the probability that the measurement of the energy will yield the value e_n.

There is no need here to consider in detail this new conception of the state of an atomic system. The only relevant question is whether this mathematical construct ϕ has those general properties which our definition of directive correlation assumed the 'state' of a physical system to have. Now the main assumptions made in defining directive correlation were the following:

(i) We assumed the 'state' of a physical system to refer to, or to specify, something *objective*, something that can be assumed to exist independently of the observer, independent of any act of observation or measurement. When we speak of a table or chair as 'objective' entities, we mean that we can assume their existence not to be contingent on our presence as observing subjects. Or, to be more precise, we mean that the assumption of their independent existence in a certain part of the room enables us to account for the sense impressions we get when we look in a certain direction in the room or explore a certain region of it by touch, and for the way these impressions respond to certain acts on our part, e.g. to our moving the eyes, or walking across the room. Similarly, by saying that the state of a physical system represents something objective we mean that the assumption of its existing independently

---

[1] See above.

of the observer, or of any measuring operation, enables us to account for the results, the pointer-readings, we get when we do carry out certain observations or measuring operations on the system in question.

In this connexion it is particularly important to realize that this does *not* imply that in order to be regarded as something *objective* the state of a physical system must be *determinable* by measuring operations. It implies no more than that for every state of a physical system there must exist at least one possible[1] set of circumstances involving the given physical system and one possible measuring operation, in which the result of the measurement[2] can be formally represented as a single-valued function of the respective state. In other words, it implies no more than that there must be at least one case in which we can reason from premises about the state of the system to conclusions about the result of a measurement. And this does *not* mean that the state of the system itself must be determinable. For the state of a system to be determinable we must be able to reason from the results of measurements to the state of the measured system, and not vice versa as above.

(ii) We assumed the 'state' of a physical system to be subject to causal determination, i.e. that every state of a physical system is a single-valued function of the system's initial state. We have already mentioned that ϕ fulfils this condition.

Now the essential point to be made is the following. Contrary to very widely held opinions, the new quantum conception of the state of a physical system *does* fulfil not only (ii) but also our requirement (i). The prevalence of a different opinion in modern philosophy and physics is due to the failure to realize the exact nature of the requirement (i). Since the quantum state of a physical system is not always determinable, it was held that it did not represent anything objective. We have seen that this is a fallacy. All that is required for the state of a system to be objective, is that there exists a set of circumstances for which a measuring operation is possible whose results can be formally represented, according to the axioms of accepted physical theories, as a single-valued function of that state. This latter condition is always fulfilled by the quantum state of a physical system, because, according to the quantum theory, the mean value of an observable in a large assembly of similar physical systems is determined by

---

[1] i.e. compatible with the axioms of accepted physical theories.
[2] In accordance with accepted physical theories.

the states of the individual systems. Hence, whenever we have an atomic system S in a certain quantum state ϕ we know that there exists a possible[1] set of circumstances for which there is a possible[1] measurement whose outcome is a single-valued function of ϕ, viz. when S is a member of a very large assembly of similar systems and a measurement is made of the mean value of an observable in the assembly.

We may therefore conclude that the idea of causally determined and objective 'states' in atomic systems is compatible with quantum theory; and that the idea of 'directive correlation' could, if necessary, also be applied to systems of atomic magnitude.

[1] See footnote 1, p. 206.

INDEX OF DEFINITIONS AND EXPLICATIONS

PRINTED IN GREAT BRITAIN
AT THE UNIVERSITY PRESS, OXFORD
BY CHARLES BATEY, PRINTER TO THE UNIVERSITY